The Open University

Block 3

Diverse communities and resources for care

This publication forms part of an Open University course, K101 *An introduction to health and social care*. Details of this and other Open University courses can be obtained from the Student Registration and Enquiry Service, The Open University, PO Box 197, Milton Keynes MK7 6BJ, United Kingdom, tel. +44 (0)845 300 60 90, email general-enquiries@open.ac.uk

Alternatively, you may visit the Open University website at www.open.ac.uk where you can learn more about the wide range of courses and packs offered at all levels by The Open University.

To purchase a selection of Open University course materials, visit www.ouw.co.uk or contact Open University Worldwide, Walton Hall, Milton Keynes MK7 6AA, United Kingdom for a brochure, tel. +44 (0)1908 858793, fax +44 (0)1908 858787, email ouw-customer-services@open.ac.uk

The Open University
Walton Hall, Milton Keynes
MK7 6AA

First published 2008

Edited and designed by The Open University.

Typeset by SR Nova Pvt Ltd, Bangalore, India.

Printed in Malta by Gutenberg Press Limited.

ISBN 978 0 7492 4644 0

1.1

Contents

Learning skills by Andrew Northedge

Introduction to Block 3

Block 3 is about communities and their connection with care. As you saw in Block 1, care often takes place in people's homes. However, families and individuals live in communities, and communities offer many kinds of care resources which people use on an informal basis to keep healthy. Unit 9, 'Improving health and well-being in neighbourhoods', explores the ways in which communities as a whole can improve people's health and well-being. Unit 10, 'Inclusion and exclusion in the community', looks at people's different experiences of community life, and considers whether a community approach can meet the needs of people who are excluded and isolated. Unit 11, 'Working with diversity', looks at the implications for health and social care services of recognising that local communities are made up of a variety of groups with a range of needs. Finally, Unit 12, 'Supporting people to use community resources' – the skills unit for this block – gives you the chance to develop skills in helping people to access and make use of local facilities and services.

Unit 9

Improving health and well-being in neighbourhoods

Prepared for the course team by Fran Wiles

Contents

Introduction

Where you live can affect your health. Unit 9 considers the ways in which communities, as a whole, can enhance people's health and well-being. Using film and audio material, you will be getting to know a real-life neighbourhood renewal programme.

Block 3 is about communities and their connection with care. So why does this unit talk about neighbourhoods? A neighbourhood is a particular kind of community with defined boundaries: a place where, for some residents, most aspects of daily life and care are experienced. Neighbourhood renewal policies make reference to both neighbourhoods and communities, and the distinction is not always obvious. Sometimes words have acquired historical associations: for example, 'community work' is an established method of working with groups of people. In exploring the case study in this unit, you will hear both words used – 'community' and 'neighbourhood' – depending on the context.

Core questions

- How do neighbourhoods affect people's well-being?
- What are poverty and social exclusion, and what impact do they have on health and well-being?
- What does neighbourhood renewal mean, and how effective is it in improving health and social care?
- What are the challenges of involving local people in neighbourhood renewal?

Are you taking the IVR?

If you are studying K101 as part of the Integrated Vocational Route (IVR), don't forget to check your VQ Candidate Handbook to see which Unit 9 activities contribute to your electronic portfolio.

1 Healthy neighbourhoods

Families and communities have always provided the backbone of informal health and social care. Since the late 1990s, however, government policies have put a particular emphasis on developing community resources to address social problems.

In Unit 9 you will be exploring the work of a neighbourhood renewal programme located on a housing estate in the south-east of England. Thornhill lies five miles east of Southampton city centre, and in 1999 it was selected to be one of thirty-nine government-funded New Deal for Communities (NDC) programmes. The programme, called Thornhill Plus You, has a wide remit, but in Unit 9 you will be using film and audio material to explore specifically its work on health and well-being.

1.1 A broad view of health

Thornhill Plus You aims to involve local people in developing services that will improve health. The programme takes a broad view of health, which is based on the World Health Organization (WHO) definition you read about in Unit 2: 'Health is a state of complete physical, mental and social well-being and not merely the absence of disease or infirmity' (WHO, 1946). Achieving 'complete' health may seem ambitious, but this definition is widely used, and in comparison with the biomedical model (which you also read about in Unit 2), takes account of the whole person. Drawing on the WHO definition, public health academic Ronald Labonte interprets the three dimensions of health and well-being – physical, mental and social – like this:

> … to experience health and well being, three things need to be in place: physical capability, including vitality and energy; mental health, essentially described as having meaning and purpose in life; and a social context of connection to family and others in the community. … people need energy and connection to others to enjoy good social relationships, connection to community and a sense of purpose to feel some control over life, and both energy and a sense of purpose to be able to live enjoyable lives.

> (Hashagen, 2003, p. 287)

Labonte's model of health and well-being is represented in Figure 1. Have a look at the circles and their intersections, and then complete the activity that follows.

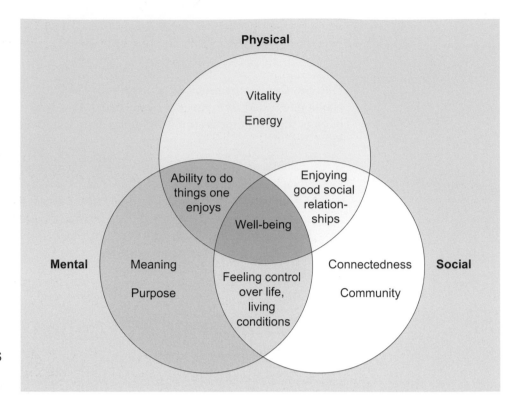

Figure 1   Labonte's model of health and well-being (Source: NHS Health Scotland, 2003, p. 7, Figure 1)

Learning skills: Reading Venn diagrams

Labonte's model of health and well-being takes the form of a Venn diagram (named after English philosopher and mathematician John Venn). A Venn diagram shows all the possible combinations of different sets of things. In this case, we see three groups of things. They are three sets of factors relating to health and well-being: 'physical', 'mental' and 'social' factors. The diagram shows what Labonte suggests are the outcomes when various combinations of these factors are in place.

- In the top part of the upper circle you see the physical factors alone – 'vitality' and 'energy'.

- In the left part of the left-hand circle you see the mental factors alone – 'meaning' and 'purpose'.

- Where these two circles overlap you see what Labonte suggests is produced when both physical and mental factors are in place.

Activity 1 will help you to check that you have grasped the idea of how Venn diagrams work.

Activity 1   Labonte's model of health and well-being

Allow about 10 minutes

Use the diagram in Figure 1 to answer the following questions:

(a) According to Labonte, what two things do people need in order to:
- be able to do things they enjoy?
- enjoy good social relationships?
- feel in control of their lives?

(b) When people can do things they enjoy *and* have good social relationships *and* feel in control of their lives, what does this add up to?

Comment

Did you come up with these answers?

(a) According to Labonte:

- To be able to do things they enjoy, people need energy (physical capability) and a sense of purpose (good mental health).
- To be able to enjoy good social relationships, people need to feel connected to others (social well-being) and to have energy.
- To feel in control of their lives, people need to feel a sense of purpose and connection to others.

(b) When people can do things they enjoy *and* have good social relationships *and* feel in control of their lives, they feel a sense of well-being.

In Thornhill's community projects, you will see that the word 'well-being' is used alongside health. The WHO definition of health describes its three components: physical, mental and social well-being. Labonte's model shows how these are interconnected. Well-being is a term which means different things to different people: it's primarily about how you feel, and is not easy to measure. However, combining the words 'health' and 'well-being' shifts the focus from a purely biomedical perspective to a much broader, holistic view of health.

1.2 Introducing Thornhill

In the next activity, you will be able to explore this broad definition of health, as you meet some of Thornhill's residents enjoying leisure activities funded by the Thornhill Plus You programme.

DVD

Activity 2   What kinds of activities promote good health?

Allow about 20 minutes

You are now going to see people enjoying three very different activities: a group called Crafty Crafters, netball sessions for women over the age of sixteen, and a tea dance in a local church hall.

Find Block 3, Unit 9, Activity 2 on the DVD.

Comment

The film about Motiv8 has given you an insight into how neighbourhood-based activities can meet a wide range of health and well-being needs. You saw people of all ages and physical capabilities. Some of the activities – netball and dancing – help to improve physical health. All of them help people to develop and maintain abilities, and get positive feedback from others. The people in the film feel good about themselves, and feel connected to others around them. They have a sense of physical, social and mental well-being.

Enhancing well-being
through leisure activities

The Thornhill residents you have seen in the Motiv8 film are taking steps to improve their health and well-being, but they are not a cross-section of the neighbourhood. In order to apply for New Deal for Communities funding, Thornhill had to be defined as an area with a high level of deprivation. Compared with other parts of Southampton and south-east England, people living in Thornhill experienced lower levels of health. In the next activity, you will be able to find out more about the health and well-being needs of Thornhill residents.

DVD

Activity 3   People in Thornhill and the disadvantages they experience

Allow about 30 minutes

You are now going to hear Dave Kellett, Director of Thornhill Plus You, and Ruth Chiddle, its Community Health Manager, talking in general terms about the people who live in Thornhill, the disadvantages they face, and the health problems they experience.

Find Block 3, Unit 9, Activity 3 on the DVD.

Comment

You now have a good idea of who lives in Thornhill and the kinds of health problems experienced there. It is a predominantly white neighbourhood, with a higher than average percentage of families with children, and a rising number of older people. There is very little employment in the area, and many people are living on a low income, including long-term disability and incapacity benefits. Some people are 'socially isolated' and 'excluded'. You have also heard that there is a Travellers' site at the edge of the Thornhill estate. Health issues in Thornhill include high rates of smoking, mental and physical ill health and teenage pregnancy.

The disadvantages faced by people in Thornhill are found in many similar neighbourhoods across the UK. Programmes like Thornhill Plus You are part of the government's response to the growing evidence that health and neighbourhoods are connected.

1.3 Factors that influence people's health

There is a wealth of research evidence – some of it published in official documents such as the Black Report (Working Group on Inequalities in Health, 1980) and the Acheson Report (Independent Inquiry into Inequalities in Health, 1998) – which shows that health is influenced by where people live.

In 1998 the Independent Inquiry into Inequalities in Health reported to the government on the connections between poor health and living in a deprived neighbourhood. The report – usually known as the Acheson Report after its author Sir Donald Acheson – presented evidence showing that every aspect of health is worse for people living in deprived circumstances. In considering the factors that influence people's health, the inquiry took a broad approach, which has many similarities with Labonte's model. However, in the extract which follows, you will see that the report calls its approach 'socioeconomic', because it takes account of social and economic conditions, as well as people's individual characteristics.

Activity 4   The Acheson Report: a socioeconomic approach

Allow about 30 minutes

The activity is in two parts.

(a) Begin by looking carefully at the diagram in Figure 2 and reading the extract given below.

Extract from the report of the Independent Inquiry into Inequalities in Health (Acheson Report)

Socioeconomic model of health

> We have adopted a socioeconomic model of health and its inequalities. This is in line with the weight of scientific evidence. … [Figure 2] shows the main determinants of health as layers of influence, one over another.

> At the centre are individuals, endowed with age, sex and constitutional factors which undoubtedly influence their health potential, but which are fixed. Surrounding the individuals are layers of influence that, in theory, could be modified. The innermost layer represents the personal behaviour and way of life adopted by individuals, containing factors such as smoking habits and physical activity, with the potential to promote or damage health. But individuals do not exist in a vacuum: they interact with friends, relatives and their immediate community, and come under the social and community influences represented in the next layer. Mutual support within a community can sustain the health of its members in otherwise unfavourable conditions. The wider influences on a person's ability to maintain health (shown in the third layer) include their living and working conditions, food supplies and access to essential goods and services. Overall there are the economic, cultural and environmental conditions prevalent in society as a whole, represented in the outermost layer.

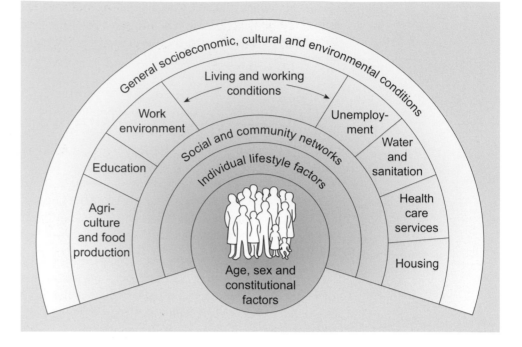

Figure 2   The main
determinants of health
(Source: Independent
Inquiry into Inequalities
in Health, 1998,
Figure 1)

The model emphasises interactions between these different layers. For
example, individual lifestyles are embedded in social and community
networks and in living and working conditions, which in turn are related to
the wider cultural and socioeconomic environment.

(Independent Inquiry into Inequalities in Health, 1998)

Acheson draws a distinction between people's personal attributes – for example,
their age and whether they are male or female – and the 'layers of influence' that
surround them. Although policy interventions can't alter individual characteristics,
they aim to modify the other factors that influence health. For example, policies
that urge people to eat healthy food and give up smoking are focused at the level
of changing people's lifestyles.

(b) To help you make sense of Acheson's socioeconomic approach, we return
now to Thornhill. For the next part of the activity you will need your responses
to Activity 3, Tasks 1 and 2, and (if you don't want to write in this book) the
diagram you printed earlier when you were doing Activity 3.

- First, you need to create an imaginary Thornhill resident, based on the
  information that Dave and Ruth gave about the population. For example,
  I thought of a single man in his thirties, unemployed due to a long-term
  illness. He is taking medication for depression. He lives alone in a
  second-floor flat with no lift. Perhaps he finds it difficult to go out and get
  some exercise. I called him Liam.

- Next, write the person's age and gender at the bottom of the diagram and
  draw a line into the small circle which says 'age, sex and constitutional
  factors'. I wrote 'Liam, a man in his 30s'.

- Now write the other information around the edge of the diagram, for
  example, 'unemployed'.

- Look at what you've written and draw lines to connect the information to
  the appropriate layers of influence. For example, 'unemployed' relates to
  the layer which says 'living and working conditions'. You can connect your
  notes to more than one layer of influence if that seems appropriate – for

example, if Liam's lack of employment causes him to be isolated, then I could also draw a line into the layer 'social and community networks'.

- Finally, look at what you've written and think about how the layers are interconnected.

Comment

Figure 3 shows the diagram I drew for Liam, my imaginary Thornhill resident. Even if you chose a similar person, you might have picked out different factors, so don't worry if your diagram looks different.

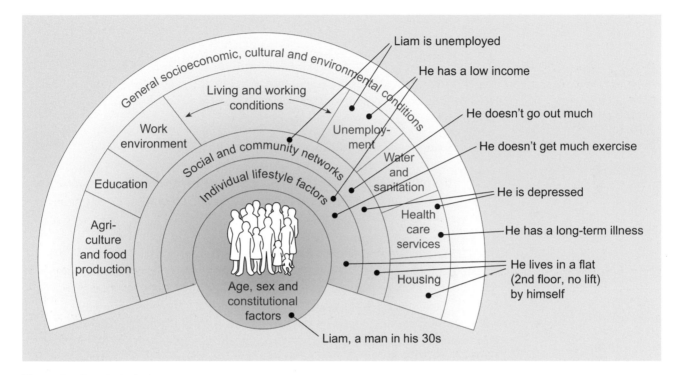

Figure 3 Annotated version of Figure 2 'The main determinants of health' – Liam

From looking at my diagram, you can see that Liam's health could be influenced by a wide range of factors. In particular, his living conditions and his unemployment seem important. Living in a second-floor flat without a lift makes it difficult for him to get out, especially if his illness affects his mobility. Not going out limits the amount of exercise he gets (not good for his physical health) and it also prevents him from making contact with other people (not good for his mental health). As he is unemployed, he doesn't have much money, which might prevent him from socialising or taking exercise. Unemployment also reduces the amount of social contact he has.

This activity should have helped you to think about some of the individual, social and economic factors that can influence health. The Acheson Report has been influential on government policies that target resources at disadvantaged neighbourhoods in an effort to reduce social and health inequalities. New Deal for Communities programmes, such as Thornhill Plus You, are a part of this strategy.

1.4 What is a 'healthy neighbourhood'?

The idea that communities can influence people's health is not new. To some extent, developments like those in Thornhill draw on the legacy of the 1970s community health movement, which, as Pat Taylor explains, 'remained outside mainstream NHS consciousness' and consisted of:

> ... health related activities in local communities ... to help local people articulate and take action on health concerns. Food cooperatives, mental health support groups, anti-tranquilliser groups, community swimming sessions, environmental clean up campaigns, women's refuges and boys' football clubs were all examples of communities' perspective on health.

> (Taylor, 2003, pp. 134–5)

Shortly after the publication of the Acheson Report, the idea of healthy neighbourhoods was introduced in a government paper about the future of the NHS in England. The paper, titled *Saving Lives: Our Healthier Nation* (1999), took the view that:

> Communities can tackle poor health, which springs ... from a range of wider, community factors – including poverty, low wages, unemployment, poor education, sub-standard housing, crime and disorder and a polluted environment.

> (Secretary of State for Health, 1999, p. 2)

Our Healthier Nation proposed that public health interventions should be targeted at three settings – healthy schools, healthy workplaces and healthy neighbourhoods – in order to reach people of all ages. The government didn't actually define what a healthy neighbourhood was, but the concept was subsequently developed by the King's Fund, an independent research organisation in London. To explore what a healthy neighbourhood looked like and how the idea might be applied in practice, the King's Fund examined what existing neighbourhood-based projects were doing to improve the health and well-being of local people. On the basis of their research, the King's Fund suggested that a healthy neighbourhood is a place:

- where people feel safe
- where the environment is clean and unpolluted
- where people feel included
- where people feel confident about expressing their health needs
- where new and creative ideas are encouraged
- which is connected to the opportunities offered by the wider community around it.

> (Adapted from Gowman, 1999)

To achieve this state, the King's Fund suggested that neighbourhoods needed certain resources. These include:

- **amenities**: including good quality housing, schools, accessible sports and leisure facilities, attractive public spaces and meeting places, shops
- **local knowledge**: based on residents' experience of what is needed, and what will work
- **services that are accessible**: public, voluntary and private organisations on site

- **employment opportunities**: workplaces in the local area
- **funding and other kinds of support**: investment in the area from statutory bodies.

(Adapted from Gowman, 1999)

In the next activity, you will think about what a healthy neighbourhood involves in practice.

DVD

Activity 5   Is Thornhill a healthy neighbourhood?

Allow about 30 minutes

You are now going to hear seven residents talking about Thornhill. As you listen to their words and view the film, you'll be able to think about how Thornhill compares with the King's Fund idea of what makes a healthy neighbourhood.

Find Block 3, Unit 9, Activity 5 on the DVD.

Comment

Thornhill illustrates many aspects of a healthy neighbourhood, and due to the developments taking place there, residents are beginning to notice improvements. They now have access to resources which help them to be healthy. Even so, it's clear that the neighbourhood doesn't yet meet everyone's needs – for example, Jill still can't get her wheelchair into some of the shops, Shelley doesn't take her children to the parks because she considers them dirty and unsafe places, and Alexis clearly finds some parts of the estate 'rough' and unwelcoming.

This busy shopping parade offers a number of resources, including a place for residents to meet informally

You will remember that Dave Kellett mentioned another section of Thornhill's community: the Travellers who live on the permanent site. Local agencies provide services there, but in some ways the Travellers form a small community of their own, within the geographical boundaries of Thornhill. They value their privacy and it wasn't possible to film them, so they don't feature on the DVD, but Travellers and their particular health needs will feature again in Units 10 and 11.

Before you finish your work for this section, you are invited to consider what you have learned in relation to a neighbourhood much closer to you.

Activity 6   Is your neighbourhood healthy?

Allow about 10 minutes

When you did Activity 5, it was suggested that you print off a copy of the Activity Notes which show, on a grid, the King's Fund characteristics of a healthy neighbourhood. This time, think about your own neighbourhood or one with which you are familiar, and complete the grid to show the presence or absence of these characteristics. How does it compare with Thornhill? If you have knowledge of two or more neighbourhoods, are there differences between what they offer in terms of resources to enhance health and well-being?

Comment

Your grid will reflect your own neighbourhood. A course tester commented:

> My parents live in a rural village, which you'd expect to be a healthy place – and in some ways it is. There's plenty of open space for children to run around. People know each other and it feels safe (though I expect it's a bit claustrophobic for teenagers). There's a community spirit and neighbours actually do look out for each other. But other things are not so good for health. There is one food shop, which is expensive and doesn't have fresh produce. The doctor only does a surgery once a week, and the nearest dentist is twenty miles away. The bus service is dreadful, and if you don't have a car you are a long way from the main shops, post office and hospital. It's very hilly and there are no real pavements – my mother has a wheelchair now, but there's no way she can go outside in it.

Your work on Activities 5 and 6 may have revealed the variation between different localities and neighbourhoods in terms of the opportunities they offer for sustaining or inhibiting health and well-being. The reason that Thornhill was eligible for neighbourhood renewal funding is that the local population as a whole experiences a high degree of social and health disadvantages, compared with other neighbourhoods in Southampton and the south-east region. Section 2 will go on to consider the nature of health inequalities more generally.

Key points

- Community health projects start from a broad view of health, which takes account of physical, social and mental well-being.
- Labonte's model of health shows that the three aspects of well-being are interconnected.
- The Acheson Report showed that health is influenced by where people live.
- The King's Fund concept of a healthy neighbourhood emphasises that a community's resources – or lack of them – can have a considerable impact on the well-being of people who live there.

Learning skills: Reading with your essay in mind

With TMA 02 only just behind you, perhaps it seems a bit much to raise the topic of your next essay right now. Yet, as you launch yourself into another block, it is a good moment to stop and think about how your essay writing fits into your studies as a whole. Did your Block 2 essay feel like a last-minute panic, or did you build up to it gradually over the previous weeks? What is the best way to build essay writing into your work on Block 3?

Is it a good idea to look at TMA 03 right now? The questions may not make complete sense to you before reading the block, but you can still try underlining key words in pencil and start jotting down a few thoughts. This will help you to recognise things that could be useful for your essay as you work through the units. If you have an 'essay' notepad, then you can keep adding in new ideas as you study the block. Then by the time you reach the writing, you will have something to build on. Being aware of the essay questions gives an extra thrust to your studies – a purpose to your reading and an edge against which to hone your thoughts.

2 Low income, health and social exclusion

In Section 1 you considered some of the factors contributing to health, and saw that where people live can have consequences for their health. We move on now to look more closely at two associated and interlinked issues for health and well-being, which have been raised by the Thornhill case study: the impact of poverty, and the effects of social exclusion.

2.1 Measuring poverty and ill health

To begin your work for this topic, look at the graph in Figure 4, which shows the rate of deaths for adults under the age of sixty-five in 2004. It compares the rate between people living in deprived neighbourhoods and those living in prosperous neighbourhoods in Scotland. Death under the age of sixty-five is defined as premature.

Don't spend too long on this: just try to get a visual grasp of the difference in the premature death rates between the '10% most deprived' and the '50% most prosperous' neighbourhoods. The learning skills box on the next page will help you to make sense of the graph.

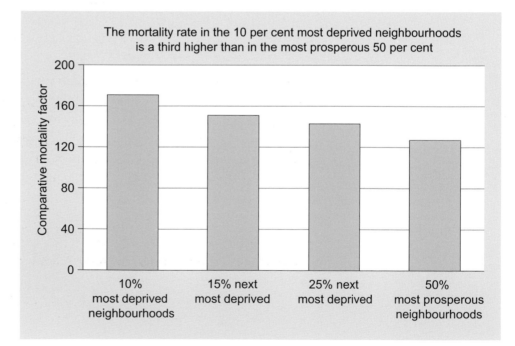

Figure 4   A comparison of premature death rates between neighbourhoods in Scotland, 2004 (Source: New Policy Institute, undated(b), www.poverty.org.uk/S35/index.shtml)

Learning skills: Reading charts

Your work on chart-reading skills in Units 4 and 8 should give you a good start in reading this bar chart. You can see from Figure 4 that these are figures for Scotland. Then, along the bottom of the chart you see that the bars represent neighbourhoods with different levels of deprivation.

- The bar at the left shows the 10% of neighbourhoods which are most deprived. (All the neighbourhoods in Scotland were given a score on the 'Scottish Index of Multiple Deprivation'. The 10% which scored lowest are shown in this bar at the left.)

- The 50% of neighbourhoods which are least deprived are shown in the bar at the right. (There is less variation between these neighbourhoods so they are all lumped together.)

- The other two bars are for the neighbourhoods in between. (Notice that if you add up 10%, 15%, 25% and 50% it comes to 100%.)

But what are the bars measuring? If you look at the left, it says 'Comparative mortality factor' (CMF). You don't need to go into how exactly this is calculated. You can just take it as meaning 'the proportion of people who die'. And the main thing is that you can see that the death rate is higher the more deprived the neighbourhood.

- You can see that the 'most deprived' bar (at the left) stands at about 170 on the CMF (perhaps a little over).

- You can see that the 'most prosperous' bar (at the right) stands at about 130 on the CMF (probably a little under)

- So the left-hand bar is over 40 higher than the right-hand bar (call it 40+).

- If three times 40 is 120, then three times 40+ will be getting on for 130. So the *difference* between the two bars (40+) is about a third of the height of the 'most prosperous' bar (130–). In other words, the most deprived bar is the height of the most prosperous bar plus one-third. This agrees with what the heading at the top of the graph tells you.

Finally, you should ask yourself 'Can I trust these statistics? Who has put the table together and where did they get the information from?' If you visit the home page of the website shown in the source line beneath the chart, you will find that it is produced by the New Policy Institute with support from the Joseph Rowntree Foundation. The website says that the graph in Figure 4 is based on government data from the new 2004 Scottish Index of Multiple Deprivation. These all seem likely to be reliable sources.

The graph shows that in the 10% most deprived neighbourhoods, the rate of premature deaths is about a third higher than in the most prosperous 50%. Put another way, if eight people were to die prematurely in the poorest neighbourhood, this would compare with six in the wealthiest neighbourhood. The graph shows average death rates based on all causes, but the discrepancy between prosperous and poor neighbourhoods is even greater for the two biggest causes of premature death, heart disease and lung cancer (which aren't actually shown here but are discussed on the website from which the chart comes). For these two health conditions, the risk of dying prematurely is dramatically higher if you are poor:

> … rates for lung cancer among people living in the most deprived areas of Scotland are three times higher than in the least deprived areas. A similar pattern emerges for coronary heart disease, with those in the most deprived areas having a risk of dying that is two and a half times [that for] those in the least deprived areas.

> (New Policy Institute, undated(b))

Premature death rates are a good way of comparing people's health in different kinds of neighbourhoods because, according to the New Policy Institute, premature death is considered to be:

> … the simplest, most accessible indicator for ill-health, being a summary measure of all major health problems which result in death. … coronary heart disease, stomach cancer and cancer of the lung, bronchus and trachea …

> (New Policy Institute, undated(b))

Three common methods are used to estimate deprivation: the Jarman Score, the Townsend Score and an overall Index of Multiple Deprivation (one for each UK nation). All these methods measure geographical populations, not individuals or social groups (see, for example, www.avon.nhs.uk/phnet/PHinfo/understanding.htm).

Thornhill was eligible to apply for neighbourhood renewal funding because of its high level of deprivation. Statistics about different kinds of disadvantage (low income, poor health, poor housing, for example) are brought together within the overall Index of Multiple Deprivation. This allows statistical information to be compared between one area and another. At the time of writing (in 2008), the most recent Index (2004) showed that the Thornhill neighbourhood was among the most deprived 10% in England, and that it was the third most deprived area in Southampton as a whole (Southampton Online, 2007).

Figure 5 shows how Thornhill compares with other neighbourhoods in England. The curved band at the top of the figure represents a continuum from the least deprived to the most deprived neighbourhood. As you can see, the pointer shows that Thornhill is at the 'most deprived' end of the scale. Underneath the curved band, the same idea of a continuum is used to give information about the different aspects of deprivation. For each factor, the dark-coloured pointer indicates the extent of Thornhill's disadvantages. The further to the right the marker is for a particular aspect, the greater the level of deprivation. Looking at the diagram, you can see that the most serious problems for people in Thornhill – compared with other neighbourhoods – relate to income, health and education.

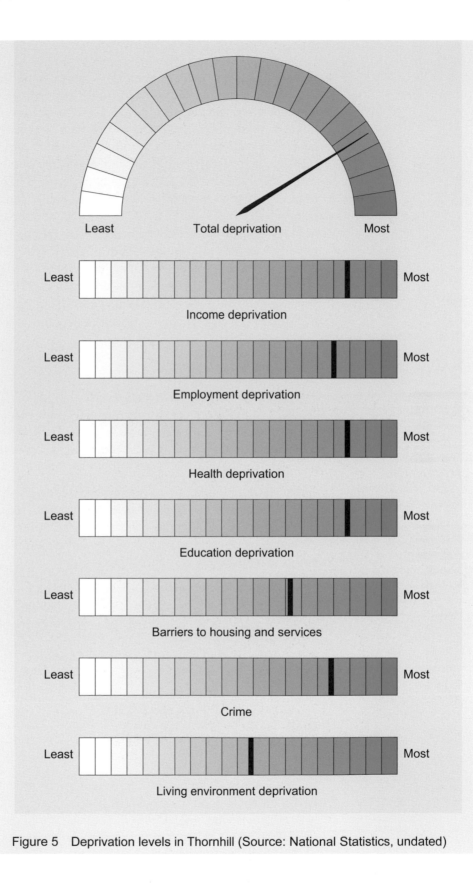

Figure 5   Deprivation levels in Thornhill (Source: National Statistics, undated)

For individuals and households, poverty can be defined and measured in a number of different ways. The two main definitions are known as 'absolute' and 'relative'.

Absolute poverty

'Absolute' poverty can be described as 'a minimum subsistence level based on essentials for survival' (Spicker, 1993, p. 2). For example, the New Policy Institute states that a widely used indicator of poverty in the developing world is 'the numbers of people living on less than $1 per day, on the grounds that people on such incomes are literally in danger of starving to death' (New Policy Institute, undated(a)). Another absolute measure of poverty, adopted by the United Nations in 1995, takes account of people's basic human needs: 'food, safe drinking water, sanitation facilities, health, shelter, education and information' (Spicker, 2007, p. 12). If a household or individual does not have access to these necessities, they are deemed to be in poverty. In the UK until around 1950, poverty was measured by the cost of a 'shopping basket' of essential items: food, housing costs and some items of clothing. Anyone who could not afford this basket of goods was defined as poor (Knight, 2005). By the 1950s, the UK was wealthier and most people could afford the basic basket of goods. This absolute measure of poverty fell out of use and was replaced by a relative definition.

Relative poverty

The relative approach holds that poverty should be defined in relation to the standard of living enjoyed by the majority of people in a society. It asks, 'How do the incomes of those at the bottom compare with the average?' Today, a widely accepted definition of poverty is 'having an income which is less than 60% of the national average' (Knight, 2005).

A relative definition of poverty is different from an absolute one because it is always dependent on fluctuations in the 'average' income, rather than a fixed figure. Relative poverty also takes account of differing circumstances and expectations across countries. Paul Spicker argues that each society has its own norms about how people should live:

> People in one society may be poor because they have no access to water or education; in another, where these are taken for granted, it may be because they do not have a warm, waterproof coat.

(Spicker, 2007, p. 15)

In the UK, poverty has become less visible than in the past. Manufactured goods have become relatively inexpensive: someone who is 'officially' poor may own a mobile phone or a television and yet go without basic requirements (Knight, 2005).

Sometimes it is hard to tell if people are poor, for as Alison Benjamin comments:

> Families with plasma screen televisions, mobile phones and the latest trainers don't fit our idea of what poverty looks like, even if they meet the official criteria of living below 60% of the median household income, and their children are going without three meals a day, school activities or adequate clothing.

(Benjamin, 2006, p. 4)

If poverty is difficult to see and define, how big a problem is it? In the early 1990s, poverty in the UK was at its highest since the 1930s. Child poverty reached a peak in 1994: statistics showed that *one child in three* was living in a poor household. This compared with only one child in ten living in similar circumstances in 1979 (Coates, 2005, pp. 19–20). By the end of the twentieth century, between a fifth and a quarter of the UK's population was living in relative poverty. At the time of writing, it is not yet clear whether poverty rates are stabilising or rising, but certainly they are not falling (Palmer et al., 2007, p. 11) and are much higher than they were in 1979.

2.2 Experiencing poverty

You have read about how poverty is measured, but how does it affect people's lives? Researchers at Sheffield Hallam University talked to people about their experiences of poverty. The men and women who took part in the research lived in deprived urban areas – mostly New Deal for Communities neighbourhoods – in Middlesbrough, Sandwell (West Midlands) and Sheffield. Most of them relied on state benefits, and the minority who were employed earned close to the minimum wage (Yeandle et al., 2003, pp. 42–6). It's likely, therefore, that they all fitted the relative definition of poverty referred to above. However, the people in the study were uncomfortable with the word 'poverty', which they associated with 'starvation and famine in other parts of the world' (Yeandle et al., 2003, p. 6). They preferred to describe themselves as living on a low income.

Reader

Activity 7   Living on a low income
Allow about 40 minutes

Read Chapter 7, 'Women and men talking about poverty, by Sue Yeandle, Karen Escott, Linda Grant and Elaine Batty in the Reader (pages 55–64). This describes the experiences of people living on a low income.

(a) Find some examples which illustrate how poverty affects:

- health (exercise, stress, nutrition, and so on)

- social relationships.

(b) As you read this account, notice whether the experiences of those who were interviewed match up to your own ideas (or your own experience) of 'being poor'. Briefly note why you think this.

Comment

(a) People talked about a wide range of topics, but I've picked out just a few examples in response to the activity question.

- **Health**. People couldn't afford fresh fruit and vegetables as much as they'd have liked. They felt under continual stress because of money worries, and this caused other problems such as loss of appetite, depression, inability to sleep, high blood pressure, heart problems and headaches. Women went without, to ensure that the men and children had essential items, such as clothes and food. People couldn't afford to take up leisure interests (and in some cases had lost the motivation and energy to go out).

- **Social relationships**. Parents talked about struggles with children when it wasn't possible to buy them things they wanted or needed; couples also argued about money. People stopped socialising with their friends, and had to avoid anyone they owed money to (including relatives). Parents felt that their children would suffer at school – or even stop attending – if they didn't have the right clothes.

(b) Course testers commented:

- The only bit that didn't match my mental image of poverty is when I read that people bought expensive clothes for their children, and that one woman said she attended a gym.

- This reminded me of my own experience of bringing up a young family on a low income – adding up my shopping bill as I went round the supermarket and having to put things back, never buying anything new, saving up for a day out and never going on holiday. The difference was that I had chosen my situation and knew it wouldn't go on for ever. When my kids got older I was able to return to work and we could afford things again. The people I read about didn't seem to have that choice.

- In my country where I grew up, the people I read about would be regarded as well off. They have televisions and go on holiday. In my country the children would be lucky to have clothes that were new.

You can see from Activity 7 that poverty is more complex than just having insufficient money. Living on a low income for long periods of time is stressful and can cause tensions in family life and other relationships. Stress and poor diet affect people's health. Limitations placed on shopping, visiting and leisure activities prevent people from taking part in important – and supportive – aspects of everyday life.

2.3 How poverty affects people's health

The Acheson Report (Independent Inquiry into Inequalities in Health, 1998), as you saw in the previous section, revealed the links between poor health and living in a deprived neighbourhood. On the DVD you heard some examples of how poverty affects the health of Thornhill residents. In Chapter 7 in the Reader, people living in other deprived neighbourhoods talked about their own experiences of poverty. These personal accounts are supported by statistical evidence about health inequalities for children and adults.

Children

For children, the impact of poverty is wide-ranging and can affect how well they do in future life. In fact, babies from low-income families are 50% more likely to die during their first year, than babies from high-income families. Babies from poor families are also more likely to have a low birthweight. In 2005, 8.5% of babies in low-income families were born underweight, compared with 6.5% of babies in higher-income families (New Policy Institute, undated(d)). Low birthweight is seen as a risk to immediate and long-term health, because there is evidence that children born underweight are more likely to develop health problems across their lifespan. Summarising this evidence, the New Policy Institute explains that:

> The rates of death and illness associated with low birth weight reflect both its immediate and its long-term health risks to the infant. It is closely correlated with poor health in the first four weeks of life, and with death before the age of two years; there are also associations with premature death from coronary artery disease [Spencer, 1996, p. 112].

Low birth weight is also associated with delayed physical and intellectual development in early childhood, and in adolescence [Carr-Hill, 1990]. Cerebral palsy, sight and hearing defects, and hernias are all more common in low birth weight babies [Botting, 1995, p. 71].

(New Policy Institute, undated(d))

In addition to low birthweight, the New Policy Institute collates statistical information about a range of child health issues, including infant death, dental health and underage pregnancy. In each case, the health of poor children is shown to be significantly worse than that of children from higher-income families (New Policy Institute, undated(c)).

People on low incomes are at greater risk of poor health and premature death

Adults

As the Acheson Report made clear, adults' health is equally affected by low income. For example, in the early 1990s, the death rate among men of working age was almost three times as high for unskilled as for professional workers. The rate of premature deaths is beginning to show a downward trend (although it is higher in Scotland than in England and Wales). Nevertheless, for health conditions such as lung cancer and heart disease, the gap between poor people and their more affluent peers remains very wide for all the UK countries (New Policy Institute, undated(f)).

The Acheson Report also drew attention to the links between low income and mental health. It was found that disorders such as anxiety, depression and phobias are more common among women in low-income groups (affecting 24% in 1993–94), compared with women in higher-income groups (affecting 15% in 1993–94). For men, there was an equally striking finding concerning alcohol misuse – 10% of men in low-income groups were dependent on alcohol, compared to 5% in higher-income groups. More recent research (2004) still shows that adults who are poor are twice as likely to be at risk of developing a mental illness as those on average incomes (New Policy Institute, undated(e)).

When people have mental health problems, they are more likely than others to have additional physical health problems. Investigating health inequalities, the Disability Rights Commission found that in England and Wales:

> … someone with a major mental health problem is more likely to develop a significant illness like diabetes, CHD [coronary heart disease], stroke or respiratory disease than other citizens, more likely to develop it before 55, and – once they have it – more likely to die of it within five years. … People with depression also have higher risks of key physical illnesses than other citizens.
>
> (Disability Rights Commission, 2007, p. 28)

It is clear, then, that across the lifespan there are inequalities in people's health which follow from their economic position. Poor people are more likely to be in poor health and to die at an earlier age.

Poverty affects not only people's health, but also their wider life opportunities. A 2006 report published by the Department for Work and Pensions (DWP) summarised research which showed that:

> Compared with those with a higher income, children experiencing poverty are:
>
> * less likely to perform well at school and more likely to play truant;
> * more likely to have lower self-esteem and lower expectations for their future;
> * more likely to be involved in criminal behaviour;
> * … more likely to smoke and drink; …
> * more likely to have a child at a young age, for young women.
>
> (DWP, 2006, p. 32)

In their adult lives, children faced with these disadvantages are likely to have low incomes, be unemployed and be in poor health (DWP, 2006). The recognition that people can experience a range of interlinked problems has given rise to the concept of 'social exclusion'.

2.4 Social exclusion

You might remember that Dave Kellett used the words 'isolated' and 'excluded' to refer to some sections of the Thornhill population. To be socially excluded means lacking opportunities and experiences that are taken for granted by the general population. This idea can be thought of in three ways:

> In practice, the idea of exclusion is mainly used in three contexts. The first is financial: exclusion is identified with poverty, and its effect on a person's ability to participate in normal activities. The second is exclusion from the labour market: exclusion is strongly identified with long-term unemployment … Third, there is exclusion in its social sense ….
>
> (Centre for Public Policy and Management, Robert Gordon University, undated)

So, people who are socially excluded may lack access to a reasonable standard of education, housing, health, employment and income. As a result of these disadvantages, they can be socially excluded in a more literal sense:

> People are excluded when they are not part of the networks which support most people in ordinary life – networks of family, friends, community and employment. Among many others, poor people, ex-prisoners, homeless people, people with AIDS, people with learning disabilities or psychiatric patients might all be said to be at risk of exclusion.

> (Centre for Public Policy and Management,
> Robert Gordon University, undated)

Social exclusion and poverty are not the same thing. The term 'social exclusion' refers to more than just low income. However, social exclusion is strongly linked with poverty, because – as you have seen – poverty affects people's opportunities in life.

In the next activity, you will be able to explore the idea of social exclusion further, using the examples described in Chapter 7 in the Reader.

Reader

Activity 8   Being excluded

Allow about 30 minutes

First of all, look back at the definition of social exclusion and remind yourself about what it means.

Now have another look at Chapter 7 in the Reader (pages 55–64). This time, find two or three examples of people being unable to afford to take part in activities with friends and family.

Draw a line vertically down the middle of a piece of paper, and list your examples down one side. Use the other side to write a few words to explain how each example illustrates social exclusion.

Comment

There are plenty of examples in Chapter 7 of people being prevented from taking part in social activities because of low income. Here are some you might have used to illustrate social exclusion.

Example	How this illustrates social exclusion
People said they hadn't been on holiday for over five years (in one case, fifteen)	Most people look forward to having a holiday. The people in Chapter 7 (especially children) won't get this opportunity. They won't be able to experience new places or activities (which is part of education in its broader sense) Families will also miss the opportunity to relax together, which helps to maintain and strengthen relationships
Parents said they couldn't afford to take their children out to the countryside, go swimming, go out for a meal or to the cinema	There might be missed opportunities to enhance physical and mental health As noted above, families miss out on spending 'special' time together, which may have a detrimental effect on relationships
People restricted or gave up their favourite sport (karate, fishing)	Missed opportunities for maintaining good physical and mental health
Some people couldn't afford to visit their families	Relationships within the extended family may suffer, and this would lead to isolation and lack of support
People avoided socialising with friends	This is detrimental to everyday social relationships and emotional support
Children and young people might be prevented from socialising with their friends, or even attending school	As well as the loss of social relationships, if children don't attend school this has negative effects for their educational progression (and future employment)

Being excluded from family and community life makes it harder to maintain supportive social relationships, and as a result people can become isolated. Chapter 7 also showed how poverty excluded people from a wide range of opportunities that are usually taken for granted in the UK. For example, some people felt 'trapped' in their neighbourhoods, unable to move away from poor housing conditions and the absence of work opportunities. They felt that employers would not take them on because of where they lived. They spoke of their health being affected by long waiting lists and inadequate health services. Children lacked play facilities. Some people didn't even feel safe in their neighbourhoods for fear of crime. Others experienced racism.

People on low incomes sometimes say they feel trapped in their neighbourhoods: unable to get jobs, to access good quality care services, or to move away to other areas

Reducing social exclusion has been a key objective of government policies since the late 1990s, and people living in deprived neighbourhoods are considered to be especially at risk. The government states that:

> Social exclusion happens when people or places suffer from a series of problems such as unemployment, discrimination, poor skills, low incomes, poor housing, high crime, ill health and family breakdown.

(Social Exclusion Taskforce, 2006)

Social exclusion doesn't only mean that poor people are likely to experience a number of simultaneous disadvantages: the key thinking that underpins the concept is that social problems are interconnected. If you are affected by one factor, you are more at risk of being affected by the others. Think back to the problems described by Dave Kellett and Ruth Chiddle. These suggest that in Thornhill, young people from poor families are more likely to leave school without qualifications or the prospect of work or training, *and* in addition may experience health problems due to poor diet, lack of exercise and underage drinking. A child growing up in a disadvantaged neighbourhood such as Thornhill might be living in poverty *and* experiencing poor housing conditions with nowhere safe to play. They might be experiencing worse than average health *and* be underachieving in school.

As you heard from Dave Kellett, it was because of the multiple problems of social exclusion that the neighbourhood was eligible for government funding. Governments have recognised that social exclusion can be addressed only by tackling the linked problems of unemployment, low qualifications, educational underachievement, crime, ill health and substandard housing, in a 'joined up way'. This means organisations – and local residents – working together to alleviate the causes and effects of all the problems, rather than working in isolation. A particular advantage of a community approach is that it encourages people to work together across traditional boundaries. 'Joined up thinking' is therefore a key characteristic of the Thornhill Plus You programme, and in Section 3 you will be considering how this works in practice.

Key points

- Poverty remains the single most important factor determining people's opportunities and quality of life.
- Poor and excluded people have a higher risk than average of experiencing health problems and dying young.
- The concept of social exclusion draws attention to the way in which poverty, health and other social problems are interlinked.
- Socially excluded people lack opportunities and experiences that are taken for granted by the general population.
- Reducing social exclusion requires a 'joined up approach', in which different people and organisations work together to address all the problems.

3 A neighbourhood approach to improving health and well-being

Let's return now to Thornhill, to find out how a neighbourhood approach can improve people's health. You will be hearing about the early days of the Thornhill Plus You programme, and continuing to explore its community health work.

3.1 Overcoming low aspirations: a challenge for neighbourhood renewal

Thornhill qualified for government funding because it was among the 10% most deprived neighbourhoods in England. As you have seen, poverty affects all aspects of people's lives and well-being. Living with poverty, unemployment and ill health for a long time has a demoralising effect, which makes the problems even worse. Dave Kellett, Director of the Thornhill Plus You programme, recognises that this presents a challenge for neighbourhood renewal:

> I would say the worst characteristic about people on Thornhill and many regeneration areas, is the characteristic of low aspiration, little hope. And that's fundamentally the thing that we've got to grapple with.

(DVD, Block 3, Unit 9, Activity 3 audio)

Lynsey Hanley, a journalist who grew up on a large council (social housing) estate on the outskirts of Birmingham, argues that low aspiration is a product of living in a place which has become associated with failure. In the next activity, you will find out why Hanley thinks this, in an extract from her book *Estates*.

Reader

Activity 9   Perceptions about council estates

Allow about one hour

Read Chapter 10, 'Estates', by Lynsey Hanley in the Reader (pages 83–88), and make notes in response to the following questions:

(a) What kinds of images does Hanley say are portrayed about people who live on council estates?

(b) What does Hanley mean by 'the wall in the head'? How has this wall affected Hanley herself and others whom we assume haven't left the estate?

(c) What remedy does Hanley suggest for overcoming the problems associated with social housing?

Comment

(a) According to Hanley, the images are all negative. She says that council estates are associated with alcoholism, drug addiction, lack of intelligence. Hanley says that newspapers and television portray council estates as dangerous places to be – they describe people as 'tough', 'desperate', 'failures', 'undeserving' and 'un-useful'.

(b) Hanley's term 'the wall in the head' refers to invisible barriers that constrain people's aspirations and ways of being, preventing them from reaching their potential in life. Hanley gives an account of the difficulties she experienced when she started sixth-form college and began to mix with people from a more privileged background. In general terms, she argues that the 'wall in the head' prevents working-class children on council estates from wanting to do well at school, with knock-on effects for other aspects of life.

(c) Hanley has a vision about the future of social housing. She argues that governments and councils need to treat social housing as something valuable, and invest more resources in its design. This includes improving the physical environment, but equally important – in Hanley's view – is to involve tenants in managing their estate. This would help people in social housing to 'feel as though the estate is theirs' and give them a sense of ownership and control.

Hanley expresses strong opinions about council estates, based on her own personal experience. If you live in social housing (or have done so in the past), your experience might be more positive. Hanley argues that council estate tenants are disadvantaged by other people's assumptions. However, she is not 'against' social housing. She acknowledges the importance of council estates in providing a decent standard of accommodation for working-class people. The problem, she argues, is that social housing is no longer valued. It has become somewhere you live when you have no other options. As a result, Hanley says that people who live on social housing estates have come to be thought of – and to see themselves – in a negative light.

Towards the end of Chapter 10, Hanley outlines her 'vision' for the future of social housing. She advocates that tenants need to feel 'a sense of ownership and control … as though the estate is theirs'. Promoting a sense of ownership and pride is a key feature of the Thornhill Plus You programme. Its own 'vision statement' declares its ambition to make Thornhill 'a place … where everyone will be proud to say they live' (Thornhill Plus You, undated, p. 5). Feeling positive about the neighbourhood is not just about housing: it also has implications for people's health. As you know from Labonte's model of health and well-being (which you looked at in Section 1), having a sense of control over life, and feeling connected to people around you, are essential for well-being.

New Deal for Communities funding has helped to improve the standard of existing social housing

3.2 New Deal for Communities

In Section 1 you were introduced to some of the community health activities funded by the Thornhill Plus You initiative. The next activity takes a step back to give you an overview of the programme, its aspirations and its achievements.

DVD

Activity 10   What is Thornhill Plus You?

Allow about 20 minutes

Find Block 3, Unit 9, Activity 10 on the DVD, where you will be watching a film about the work of Thornhill Plus You.

Comment

As you have heard from Dave Kellett, the government has given the Thornhill Plus You programme around £50 million to be spent on 'regenerating' Thornhill over a ten-year period. Local people were consulted about the neighbourhood's health priorities. They have been involved in designing and running the activities.

Under the government's New Deal for Communities initiative, thirty-nine severely deprived neighbourhoods across England were given time-limited funding to explore and test out innovative ways of tackling social exclusion and reducing the inequalities between their neighbourhoods and the rest of the country. As Dave Kellett explained, the government has set out five broad targets for Thornhill and other New Deal for Communities programmes. These are to:

- improve people's health
- increase educational achievement and skills
- improve housing and the physical environment
- increase the number of people in work
- reduce crime.

(Adapted from Social Exclusion Unit, 2001, pp. 9–10)

This unit is focusing on just one of Thornhill Plus You's objectives: *to improve people's health.*

New Deal for Communities is part of the government's broader strategy for neighbourhood renewal. It builds on previous policy initiatives dating back to the 1960s. (Next time you are using the DVD, you may be interested to read 'The bigger picture on regeneration' by Mithran Samuel, which is an optional media resource to accompany Block 3, Unit 9, DVD Activity 10.) What defines New Deal for Communities, however, is its emphasis on involving local people:

> ... working from the grassroots, finding bottom-up rather than top-down solutions.

(Office of the Deputy Prime Minister, 2003)

The Thornhill Plus You programme began by consulting local residents about their health concerns. In the early days of the programme, Sandra Jordan, who has lived on the estate for many years, became a member of the Community Health Group. This group brought local people and community health professionals together, to decide how the health share of the funding should be spent. Sandra knew, from her experience of bringing up her family, what was missing on the estate:

> The Community Health Group in the beginning … brought up projects that we felt were of need on our estate. Things to do with healthy eating, teenage pregnancy, midwifery, which we didn't have midwives on our estate. Dentists, which we didn't have dentists at all. All those things that we felt that we needed to have a decent health.

> (DVD, Block 3, Unit 9, Activity 10, introduction to film)

As a result, Thornhill Plus You set the following targets for improving local people's health:

- reducing the number of teenage pregnancies in Thornhill
- encouraging healthier eating
- supporting people to give up smoking
- improving the physical and mental health of residents
- improving access to health services in Thornhill.

> (Adapted from Thornhill Plus You, undated)

Another member of the Community Health Group was Ruth Chiddle, who had long experience as a health visitor in Thornhill. You may recall that in Activity 3, she explained that the group selected these targets because:

> … if you tackle those things, then you actually tackle a lot about ill health. If you tackle the smoking and the eating, and the exercise, then you're actually going to reduce your heart disease, and disease from stroke and cancer.

> (DVD, Block 3, Unit 9, Activity 3 audio)

To achieve its health targets, Thornhill Plus You works in partnership with a range of local organisations. You are now going to look more closely at one of these: the Thornhill Health and Wellbeing Project.

A locally agreed health target is to encourage people to eat 'five pieces of fruit and veg a day'

3.3 Addressing health needs and social exclusion through neighbourhood projects

The 'grassroots' approach favoured by New Deal for Communities programmes is evident in the Thornhill Health and Wellbeing Project. Known locally as THAWP, this small, neighbourhood organisation sets up and supports activities to help residents improve their health and well-being. Located in the main shopping parade, THAWP's premises are central and accessible. The project employs two Thornhill residents – Lynda Barnes and Gwyneth Baker – as community health development officers. The project is managed by Dave Shields, Strategic Services Manager at Southampton City Council. In the next activity, you will find out what THAWP is doing to help Thornhill Plus You achieve its health priorities.

DVD

Activity 11   The work of the Thornhill Health and Wellbeing Project (THAWP)

Allow about 40 minutes

Find Block 3, Unit 9, Activity 11 on the DVD. Here you will be able to view a film about the work of the Thornhill Health and Wellbeing Project. After this, you listen to Dave Shields and Gwyneth Baker talking about how the project developed and what it has achieved.

Comment

As you heard from Dave Shields, the idea for THAWP came from discussions between local people and statutory organisations in the early days of the Thornhill Plus You programme. Although THAWP is managed by the local authority, it is seen very much as a resident-led organisation. By employing two experienced and skilled Thornhill residents, it is able to develop activities that are relevant to local people's needs, with the support of trained volunteers. THAWP helps Thornhill Plus You to meet its health and well-being targets, but for local residents the successes mean more than this. From the film you saw that THAWP's activities help people to lead healthier lives, and they also address the effects of poverty and social exclusion.

As part of its health promotion work, the Thornhill Health and Wellbeing Project offers local residents free advice about safety in the home

A 'joined up approach'

To address the multiple disadvantages of social exclusion, government policies emphasise the need for a 'joined up approach'. This emphasis is reflected in New Deal for Communities programmes, which place importance on partnership working between agencies. An example of this is the collaboration between THAWP and the Thornhill Family Support Project.

The Family Support team provides a home visiting service to give practical help to families who have been identified – by social workers, midwives, health visitors and school nurses – as needing extra support. It also holds drop-in play sessions in the Eastpoint Community Centre and the Centre for Healthy Living, where any parent can get informal advice from health professionals while their young children enjoy playing. You will read more about the Locality Family Workers in Unit 10.

As you heard on the DVD, Gwyneth Baker developed the idea of the Cooking Pots sessions with Pat Hawkins, the coordinator of the Family Support Project. Gwyneth explained:

> Her remit is to work with young mums, and one of my remits is to get people to eat five fruit and veg a day, and to eat more healthily.

(DVD, Block 3, Unit 9, Activity 11 film)

By working together, the Family Support Project and THAWP have been able to provide a better service. As you have seen, young mums Shelley and Cheree value the practical help offered by the Cooking Pots sessions; however, these would not be possible without the involvement of the family support workers who play with the children while the parents are in the kitchen. As Cheree says:

> We can just focus on our cooking and know that our children are OK and they're happy playing.

(DVD, Block 3, Unit 9, Activity 11 film)

Parents and children both enjoy the Cooking Pots sessions at the community centre

Local residents working with the primary care trust

Another example of joint working is the partnership between the Thornhill Plus You programme and the Southampton City Primary Care Trust (PCT).

In England, primary care trusts (PCTs) manage the whole range of primary care services. As you found out in Unit 2, primary care services are those you normally use when you first have a health problem, and include GPs, dentists, opticians and pharmacists. NHS Walk-in Centres and the NHS Direct phone service are also part of primary care (NHS Direct, 2008). Primary care trusts work with local authorities and other agencies to make sure that a community's health and social care needs are met. You can read more about PCTs – and equivalent organisations in Wales, Northern Ireland and Scotland – in the box below.

About primary care trusts

Primary care trusts (PCTs) are the cornerstone of the NHS locally. Their equivalents in Scotland, community health partnerships, manage primary and community health services, as do local health boards in Wales. Northern Ireland is proposing to create seven local commissioning groups that will be driven by GPs.

PCTs run some primary and community services or commission them from other providers, and are involved in commissioning secondary care. PCTs are now responsible for more than 85 per cent of the NHS budget.

PCTs have three main functions:

- improving the health of the community – assessing its health needs and preparing plans, tackling health inequalities and leading partnership working with local authorities and others
- developing primary and community health services – managing and integrating all medical, dental, pharmaceutical and optical primary and community services, as well as ensuring their quality
- commissioning services, either by themselves or in partnership with a local authority, or through devolving indicative budgets to practice-based commissioners.

PCTs must work collaboratively, involving patients and the public as well as their own GP practices and partners. They must co-ordinate all agencies delivering healthcare in their area, taking responsibility for creating strong local partnerships to address the broader influences on health, and be ready to work with each other across boundaries. Strategic health authorities are responsible for managing the performance of PCTs.

(NHS Confederation, 2007)

Do you remember the Community Health Group, set up as part of the Thornhill Plus You programme to decide what the New Deal for Communities funding should be spent on? It was agreed that Thornhill Plus You would help to finance the building of a Centre for Healthy Living, in order to provide much needed primary care services in the neighbourhood. It was through the Community Health Group that local residents, like Sandra Jordan, were able to work with the PCT to design the building and the services it would offer.

The Centre for Healthy Living is now up and running, but the Community Health Group continues to bring together Thornhill residents and representatives from the PCT and Southampton City Council. In return for the Thornhill Plus You funding, the PCT provides an annual sum of money for residents to develop their own health projects. The Community Health Group, now chaired by Sandra, considers applications from local groups and decides how the money should be allocated.

Opposite is an extract from a Thornhill Plus You newsletter, showing eight community projects which have benefited from PCT funding. You can see that they are far more wide-ranging than the services you would usually expect to find in mainstream health provision.

CASH INJECTION FOR LOCAL HEALTH PROJECTS

Eight health projects in Thornhill have received a total of over £42,000 from the Southampton City Primary Care Trust. The money is being administered through Thornhill's Community Health Group, which is part of the Centre for Healthy Living project. The Community Health Group was set up in 2006 to allocate funds to projects that have a health focus in Thornhill. It comprises of representatives from the local community, the Primary Care Trust, Southampton City Council and Thornhill Plus You. Below is a summary of each of the 8 projects.

The British Trust Conservation Volunteers' Green Gym will provide an introduction to physical and health improvement, by working with local residents on environmental conservation activities to improve green spaces.

Claptrap Productions will work with young people to produce a one-minute animated film, designed to promote a greater awareness of safer sex.

Thornhill Primary School will run a Healthy Eating project, that will provide free fruit to all the school's pupils at break times, as well as running healthy eating workshops for parents.

Healthy eating is again on the menu when the Thornhill Health and Wellbeing Network (THAWN) deliver their 'Cook and Eat' sessions, which promote affordable ways of eating more healthily.

The group 'Reality!' will manage another project designed for young people. They will work with young people to develop and maintain a website that provides useful information about teenage pregnancy and parenthood.

The Sing For Your Life project will establish a Silver Song Club for the over 60s and a Community Choir for any Thornhill resident over the age of 17. Community singing stimulates both mental and physical activity and encourages greater social interaction.

The Star project will develop 'Star' sessions at Hightown and Kanes Hill primary schools, which are designed to help pupils understand how to develop positive relationships and improve self-esteem.

Treasure Gymnastics' project, the Little Treasures Gym Bus, will deliver a variety of family exercise sessions, including parent and child gymnastics and trampoline sessions.

Members of the Community Health Group would like to invite more residents to join them, to help allocate the next round of funding later this year. So, if you are interested, or if you represent an agency, charity or community group, and have an idea for a health project in Thornhill, then please contact Paula Windebank at Thornhill Plus You on 023 8091 5402 or email pwindebank@thornhillplusyou.co.uk.

six Thornhill Plus You Freephone 0800 169 5561 Community Website www.thornhillplusyou.co.uk

This extract from the Thornhill Plus You newsletter shows some of the neighbourhood health projects which have been allocated funds by a group of local residents

---

Activity 12   Supporting residents' ideas for health projects

Allow about 20 minutes

Look at the extract 'Cash injection for local health projects'. Read the short descriptions of each project and think about the different ways in which each one is likely to: (a) improve people's health and well-being; and (b) reduce social exclusion. Use the grid below to help you (in some cases there may be overlap between the columns – if so, write your ideas where you think they fit best).

Project	How will it improve people's health and well-being?	How will it reduce social exclusion?
Green Gym		
Claptrap		
Thornhill Primary School's Healthy Eating project		
'Cook and Eat' sessions		
Reality		
Sing For Your Life		
Star project		
Treasure Gymnastics		

Comment

Compare your ideas with those given in the grid below.

Project	How will it improve people's health and well-being?	How will it reduce social exclusion?
Green Gym	The activities are good for physical and mental health	This will encourage people to feel a sense of belonging and pride in their neighbourhood People will not be excluded from fitness activities because of their low incomes
Claptrap	This will promote safer sex (important for physical health). Working on the project will be good for young people's mental and social well-being	Young people will learn new skills, and get a sense of achievement. This may help them to progress with school and further education
Thornhill Primary School's Healthy Eating project	The workshops will help parents learn about healthy eating (important for physical well-being). Meeting parents in similar circumstances is also good for social and mental well-being. Children will be able to have healthy snacks at school	The workshops bring people together and reduce isolation Families with low incomes are not excluded from local 'healthy eating' initiatives
'Cook and Eat' sessions	These sessions will help people to eat healthy food. Cooking and eating with others is good for social and mental well-being too	The sessions bring people together, and are probably not expensive
Reality	Working on the project will be good for young people's social and mental well-being. The website will help teenage parents to stay healthy during pregnancy; it will also help both the parents and their babies to stay healthy afterwards. It may also help young people who are not parents to make informed choices (and thus reduce unplanned teenage pregnancies)	The website will provide support for teenage parents, so they will be less isolated. Working on the project will give young people new skills and a sense of achievement, which may help them in school and further education
Sing For Your Life	Coming together to sing will be good for mental and social well-being (and physical health too)	People on low incomes will not be excluded from joining in neighbourhood activities
Star project	This will improve children's and young people's mental and social well-being	Developing better relationships with others will improve children's and young people's self-esteem. They will feel part of their wider peer group
Treasure Gymnastics	Gymnastics will increase physical and mental well-being for children and parents	Probably a low-cost activity, so a good way for families on a low income to enjoy leisure activities together

By working with local residents in the Community Health Group, the PCT is able to support a very wide range of non-traditional health projects. As you saw in Activity 12, this has real benefits for people's health in Thornhill, and it also helps to address the effects of poverty and prevent social exclusion. The advantages are two-way: there are clear gains for the PCT too. Ruth Chiddle explains that by working with the Community Health Group, the PCT is able to try out new ways of using its budget more effectively. She comments:

> When it comes to change at the margins, it's not always easy to achieve and to plan spending for. And so I think the Primary Care Trust does appreciate this area of work … it's another way … [to] make a difference that is tailor made for an area, as opposed to just imposing on an area a way of working.

(Ruth Chiddle, interview, 22 March 2007)

Meeting Thornhill's specific challenges is important because as you have seen, PCTs are required to ensure that a community's needs are being met. However, the PCT is responsible for providing all the primary care and hospital-based health services across the whole of Southampton, and it is not hard to imagine that – without the kind of local innovation facilitated by the Community Health Group – the needs of a single neighbourhood might easily be overlooked.

Through its neighbourhood projects, the Thornhill Plus You programme is bringing about significant improvements in health. The new services and activities in Thornhill have been designed to meet the health and well-being needs identified by local residents themselves. They also help to reduce the effects of poverty and meet the needs of people who might otherwise be socially excluded: for example, young parents and their children, and vulnerable older people.

One of the programme's particular strengths is its success in engaging with local people: fostering a sense of ownership, community spirit and pride in the Thornhill neighbourhood. On a practical level, neighbourhood involvement is a real asset: it ensures that services are run by people who understand local needs. The next and final section of Unit 9 looks more closely at the advantages – and also some of the challenges – of involving local people in community-based services.

Key points

- Neighbourhood renewal is a strategy for tackling social exclusion and reducing inequalities.

- An important part of the strategy is its grassroots approach, involving local residents in all aspects of planning and delivering services.

- When neighbourhood renewal reflects local needs and priorities, it can make a real contribution to improving people's health and well-being, and reduces the effects of poverty and social exclusion.

- A 'joined up approach', where people and agencies work together, leads to more creative and effective services.

4 Local involvement as a resource

In Thornhill, neighbourhood newsletters and posters in shop windows continually urge residents to join committees, take part in surveys and questionnaires, and become volunteers with groups like THAWP. You can see some examples below. The success of the Thornhill Plus You programme relies on a high degree of local participation: let's find out what this entails.

4.1 Why do people get involved in their neighbourhood?

Involving and engaging local residents is a distinguishing feature of the New Deal for Communities approach; it is also a government requirement. This is considered to make the strategy more effective, as Dave Kellett explains:

> There is certainly evidence – not surprisingly, it's not rocket science – to show that if you have local involvement, local ownership, then the thing is actually going to work better. So the government was really clear for New Deal for Communities, that it had to be resident led.
>
> And so we have a Board which comprises twenty people. Twelve of that Board … are residents. My boss is that Board, I report to the Chair of that Board, who is a resident.
>
> (Dave Kellett, interview, 22 March 2007)

As a policy, this sounds persuasive, but how realistic is local involvement? What makes people give up their own time to support their neighbourhood in this way?

ARE YOU A DAD, STEPDAD, UNCLE OR GRANDDAD?

THEN WE NEED YOU TO TALK TO US ABOUT YOUR NEEDS AS MEN PLAYING A SIGNIFICANT ROLE IN CHILDREN'S LIVES. DO YOU WORRY ABOUT THEM MIXING WITH "THE WRONG SORT" OR BEING INVOLVED WITH DRUGS OR DRINK? MANY CHILDREN ALSO GROW UP WITHOUT A MALE ROLE MODEL.

HOW CAN WE SUPPORT YOU?

There is an opportunity to be a part of developing a men's support group and putting on activity sessions.

On Wednesday April 5th there will be an "event" at St Christopher's Church.

So please, if you would like to get involved then contact Geoff on 023 8044 8537 or Pat on 023 8043 7169.

DUMBLETON'S COPSE IS A FANTASTIC AREA OF WOODLAND ALONG THE EDGE OF THORNHILL!

The 'Friends of Dumbleton's Copse' group is keen to hear from you if you would like to get involved with looking after it.

Contact Gary Curtis on **023 8091 5002** or email him at **gary.curtis@southampton.gov.uk** for more information.

Your Block Needs You!

Around 30 of the walk-up blocks in Thornhill have a block representative, and we would like to hear from anyone interested in becoming a representative for where they live. For further information please contact Michele Exton (Tenant Involvement Officer) on **023 8091 5007** or email **michele.exton@southampton.gov.uk**.

Thornhill residents are continually being urged to become volunteers and take part in community projects

In the next activity, you will hear three Thornhill residents talking about their experiences of getting involved in neighbourhood activities. Gwyneth Baker, as you know, is now a paid community health worker with the Thornhill Health and Wellbeing Project, but she has a long history of volunteering. June Dingle chairs the network of volunteers (known as THAWN), who assist THAWP in its work, and Pauline Vaughan organises the t'ai chi sessions and helps with Cooking Pots. You will also hear Dave Kellett offer his own perspective on residents' involvement.

DVD

Activity 13   Experiences of getting involved in providing services

Allow about 30 minutes

Find Block 3, Unit 9, Activity 13 on the DVD, where you will be able to listen to Gwyneth, June and Pauline talking about their work in the neighbourhood. You then hear Dave Kellett's own thoughts about involving local people.

Comment

Gwyneth, Pauline and June are all very committed to Thornhill. Pauline started to get involved with THAWP after having a stroke, first joining the groups and eventually becoming a volunteer. This has given her back her confidence. As well as being a volunteer, June has the difficult task of recruiting others. Dave Kellett values residents' involvement, but accepts that the process takes time, and also that some people don't want to get involved.

Community health organisations depend on the active involvement of local volunteers

People have varied motivations for doing voluntary work (Bowers et al., 2006). For some, the most important thing is a sense of satisfaction with doing something useful: perhaps this is what motivates Pauline? Others find volunteering an enjoyable way of spending their time and making new friends. Voluntary work is also a way to gain new skills and knowledge, perhaps in preparation for paid work. It's possible that Gwyneth's extensive experience as a volunteer helped her to gain employment as a community worker. In some cases, voluntary work is undertaken as an alternative to paid work due to ill health or disability. As Gwyneth pointed out in Activity 11, THAWP couldn't achieve what it does without the help of volunteers. However, involving people in local community work – whether paid or unpaid – is not without its challenges.

As chair of the volunteer network, June finds it 'nigh on impossible' to recruit new members. This is not unusual: researcher Deborah Quilgars reports similar experiences in recruiting volunteers to provide care services in Hull. She found that:

> The lack of volunteers proved to be an intractable problem … most respondents … felt that community apathy and cynicism was still the prevailing attitude.

(Quilgars, 2004, p. 33)

The difficulty of recruiting volunteers, especially in areas of high need, is not new. A study of informal neighbourhood care in the late 1980s found that:

> Volunteers were … most plentiful where they were least needed, and vice versa. In particular we found there to be a dearth … of volunteers in areas containing large numbers of old, isolated and poor people.

(Snaith, 1989, p. 32)

According to current research, the two most common reasons for not getting involved in voluntary work are that people don't have the time, and that they don't think they have the necessary skills (CSV, 2005; WRVS, 2007). Andrew Thomas et al. (1999) found that some people don't know anything about voluntary work, or are put off by negative perceptions of volunteers as 'do-gooders'. Having domestic responsibilities, and feeling unable to afford expenses such as travel and food, are also reported to be barriers, while some people don't like the idea of working for no pay. In addition, Thomas and his colleagues found that unemployed people felt that voluntary work would prevent them finding a paid job, and people receiving social security benefits were afraid these might be affected.

In June Dingle's experience, another reason that people hold back is that they have become disillusioned with previous community projects because it takes a long time to see results.

4.2 Local people and agencies working in partnership

Although neighbourhood renewal policies emphasise the importance of involving local people in planning and delivering projects, there can be obstacles in practice.

Who takes the lead?

Getting people to take part is only one of the challenges. June also makes the point that it isn't easy for local residents to work with professionals because, she observes, 'they want to take it over and run it' (Block 3, Unit 9, Activity 13 audio). This experience is quite common. Researching New Deal for Communities programmes in London and Brighton, Adam Dinham found that local people were disappointed with how little power they had. As one resident explained:

> We thought we'd really be in the lead but often we feel like we're working really hard but not getting the rewards of making our own decisions.

(Dinham, 2006, p. 9)

Dinham also found that when residents tried to get involved in decision making, they were intimidated by the formality of meetings:

> Many reported feeling 'put off' by styles of meetings and the venues in which they are held … they felt disempowered … and held back from speaking at meetings for fear of appearing foolish.

(Dinham, 2005, pp. 306–7)

Making decisions

In Section 4.1 you read that Dave Kellett, the Programme Director, is responsible to a 'Board': the Thornhill Plus You Partnership Board. The people on the Partnership Board are not the staff of Thornhill Plus You, but a group of elected members. Dave mentioned that there were twenty people in this group, but at the time of writing this had increased to twenty-one people. Twelve of these are residents (including the Chair) and nine are 'agency members' (who come from local organisations). In the next activity, you will be able to find out who the Board members are, and what they do. You then hear Ruth Chiddle reflecting on what statutory (mainstream) agencies have learned about working in partnership with local people. Finally, Dave Shields talks about some of the challenges for local people working with statutory agencies.

DVD

Activity 14 Making the decisions in Thornhill Plus You

Allow about 40 minutes

Find Block 3, Unit 9, Activity 14 on the DVD. You will be able to find out about the Thornhill Plus You Partnership Board, and think about some issues involved in decision making at the neighbourhood level.

Comment

You will have recognised some familiar faces among the Thornhill Plus You Partnership Board members: Rachel, Sandra, Jill and Lynda, all local residents whom you have seen in the films. Being a member of the Board is a big responsibility and requires commitment. The twelve resident members and nine 'agency' members have been elected for a four-year period in order to make decisions about, and oversee, the future development of the Thornhill Plus You programme.

As Ruth outlined, there has been 'learning on both sides' about how local people can be effectively and genuinely involved in the Partnership Board.

It's not all plain sailing, however. Dave Shields explained that the Thornhill Health and Wellbeing project has faced scepticism from statutory agencies, who don't trust a small, neighbourhood organisation to run its own affairs.

Barriers to involvement

Pat Taylor, writing about the involvement of 'lay' members of the public in planning public health services, says that ordinary people can make an important contribution by 'drawing on the resources of their own perspectives, experiences and knowledge' (Taylor, 2003, p. 128). However, she argues that the ways in which professionals go about their business can act as barriers to prevent ordinary people's perspectives from being fully valued and taken into account. Taylor outlines the following problems:

- **Professionals define the agenda**. Professionals set the terms for discussing health, and may focus their attention on the issues defined by government targets. These are not necessarily the same issues that local people feel concerned about. For example, Taylor refers to a health professional who reported back from a public consultation: 'all they wanted to talk about was dog dirt'. Because of professional dominance, lay people usually find it easier to get involved with local health issues such as cleaning up a public area.

- **Education is not seen as a two-way process**. Professionals emphasise the need for the public to be 'educated' in order to participate, but they fail to recognise that the finding-out process should be two-way. While the public need relevant information and may require support to participate, professionals also need to learn how to work with the public. To begin with, says Taylor, professionals need to pay attention to their use of jargon, which gets in the way of partnership working.

- **Involvement is seen as a way of keeping people quiet**. Professionals may regard involvement as a way of letting people 'have their say', with no intention of taking lay views seriously.

- **Tokenism**. Professionals may see involvement as just a way of ticking monitoring sheets.

- **Incorporation**. Once lay representatives have been co-opted into an organisation's committees and projects, they can become absorbed into its culture. The particular experiences and expertise which drew them into the organisation are not utilised. Eventually, lay members' views may even be dismissed as unrepresentative because they are considered to be too knowledgeable and articulate to represent the 'average' member of the public.

- **Exploitation**. Professionals may expect lay representatives to give their time and effort voluntarily, without recognising the difficulties and costs – in terms of time and money – involved.

(Adapted from Taylor, 2003, p. 139)

Professionals need to pay attention to their use of jargon, which gets in the way of partnership working

Overcoming the barriers

Before you finish your work for this section, take some time to review the barriers summarised by Taylor, in the light of what you have learned about local involvement in Thornhill Plus You. For the next activity, you will find it useful to draw on all the Thornhill materials viewed and heard so far. There is no need to replay the DVD – just refer back to your notes on the activities.

Activity 15   Evaluating involvement in Thornhill Plus You

Allow about 20 minutes

(a) Remind yourself about the barriers which Taylor suggests can lead to lay people's perspectives being undervalued and overlooked. Then look back at your notes for Activities 13 and 14, and find two or three examples of where this either does or doesn't happen in Thornhill. Use the grid below to assist you, but remember that you don't need to find something for each box. The first row has been partly filled in as an example, but you can add to it.

(b) Finally, taking a different coloured pen, go back over your responses and highlight the practical measures which make local people's involvement successful.

Barriers to full participation	Does it happen in Thornhill?
Professionals defining the agenda	This does seem to happen sometimes. The main example is probably the conflict about smoking cessation (Activity 14), where professionals and residents had different opinions
Professionals putting emphasis on educating the public about how to participate, without seeing the need for a two-way 'finding out' process	
Seeing involvement as a way of letting people have their say, without taking their views seriously	
Incorporating lay people into the organisational culture, and ignoring their connections with the communities they come from	
Exploiting lay representatives by expecting them to give up their time and effort voluntarily	
Dismissing and discounting the views of lay people who get involved, seeing them as unrepresentative	

Comment

(a) Here are my ideas – you may have selected other examples.

Barriers to full participation	Does it happen in Thornhill?
Professionals defining the agenda	This does seem to happen sometimes. The main example is probably the conflict about smoking cessation (Activity 14), where professionals and residents had different opinions Perhaps you also noticed that residents and professionals use similar language to describe local health needs. Local needs – healthy eating, giving up smoking, taking more exercise, and so on – bear a strong resemblance to wider government health advice. Does this indicate that local agendas are set – to some extent at least – by national priorities? On the other hand, it could be that local people learn to use the same language as professionals, so that they can take part on more equal terms
Professionals putting emphasis on educating the public about how to participate, without seeing the need for a two-way 'finding out' process	There's no evidence of this happening. Although residents' attempts to participate are supported in Thornhill, Ruth says (Activity 14) that the learning has been 'on both sides'
Seeing involvement as a way of letting people have their say, without taking their views seriously	This doesn't usually seem to be the case, although Dave Shields talks about statutory agencies not trusting residents to run services. However, from what Ruth says, residents' views are taken seriously in the Board meetings. Ruth says it's important to avoid just 'ticking boxes' by having residents on committees without supporting them to take part
Incorporating lay people into the organisational culture, and ignoring their connections with the communities they come from	There's no indication of this happening. Residents get involved in pairs, so perhaps this helps them to hold on to their identities and remain visible
Exploiting lay representatives by expecting them to give up their time and effort voluntarily	This must happen at least some of the time, because June clearly feels 'officials' take no notice of volunteers' other commitments
Dismissing and discounting the views of lay people who get involved, seeing them as unrepresentative	There is no evidence of this happening – as noted above, it probably helps that residents aren't expected to attend meetings by themselves

(b) What measures did you pick out, for making local involvement successful? Compare your ideas with the ones described below.

Involving local people is not without its practical challenges, but Activity 15 suggests that the Thornhill Plus You programme generally makes a good job of it. There are some problems; for example, it's not easy to encourage people to take part. And June felt that meetings are not always arranged at times which recognise residents' family and other commitments. Nevertheless, there has been successful learning about how mainstream organisations and residents can work together. Reviewing the DVD material and Activity 15, here are some of the factors which contribute to this:

- Residents chair the Partnership Board meetings, and also chair many of the working groups (such as the Community Health Group).

- Residents are never expected to get involved alone: there are always two or more in a group, so that they can support each other.

- When they get involved in meetings, residents are helped to understand the wider picture, including the factors that need to be taken into account when decisions are made.

It is clear from what you have heard and seen in this unit that community-based initiatives bring significant benefits for the people who live there. Despite the challenges for local people of working with professional agencies, in his study of New Deal for Communities programmes, Dinham concluded that:

> … it is … evident that NDC can have some sort of significant impact on the local community. There is real growth in people's individual confidence and self-esteem and in interpersonal relationships at informal levels.
>
> (Dinham, 2005, p. 310)

Thornhill Plus You has achieved a lot since its beginnings. Think back to the films and remember Jill's satisfaction at seeing the improvements in Thornhill's social and physical environment, and Pauline's enhanced health and confidence through t'ai chi, and enthusiasm for her work with THAWP. These are just a few examples of how people's physical, mental and social well-being are being improved as a result of the Thornhill Plus You programme. Improving health, across the neighbourhood as a whole, goes a long way to reducing the health inequalities between Thornhill residents and their counterparts in the rest of Southampton.

Reflecting on the programme's success, Director Dave Kellett is particularly pleased with the way in which people and agencies in Thornhill work together:

> I think what people might not see, is that behind the scenes we are now a much more effective and influential organisation. Our Board is cohesive. They really do work together. Local partners are working very closely with us. We've been accepted, not as an irritant with this money that's suddenly been parachuted into [the neighbourhood]. But actually as an organisation that gets things done, in partnership with others. So I'm really pleased about that.
>
> (Dave Kellett, interview, 22 March 2007)

Key points

- Involving and engaging local residents is a government requirement for New Deal for Communities programmes.

- Neighbourhood health projects rely on a high degree of local participation, which takes time to develop.

- Professionals do not always take public involvement seriously, and this prevents local people's perspectives from being heard.

- Public involvement brings benefits for both local people and agencies, but it needs to be supported and it requires learning on both sides.

Conclusion

In Unit 9, you have considered the role that communities (often based around neighbourhoods) can play in influencing and supporting people's health. This was approached through the case study of Thornhill Plus You, a New Deal for Communities programme which is part of the government's neighbourhood renewal strategy. The programme's community health work draws on a holistic view of health, which includes physical, social and mental well-being. Comparing the case study with research about health inequalities, you saw that people's health is affected by poverty and deprived neighbourhoods.

In the two readings for this unit, you saw that people in deprived circumstances can be cut off from opportunities taken for granted by others. This is known as social exclusion, and it is more likely to be experienced in poor neighbourhoods. Poor neighbourhoods have also come to be associated with negative assumptions about the people who live there. All in all, one of the biggest challenges for neighbourhood renewal is to address the problem of people's low aspirations.

In the film and audio recordings, you saw how neighbourhood projects, starting from a locally defined set of priorities, can bring about significant improvements in people's health and well-being. They also help to reduce the disadvantages caused by poverty and social exclusion. Neighbourhood renewal depends on high levels of local involvement, which can be effective only if agencies are committed to learning and developing together with residents.

Overall, it is clear that community health projects and neighbourhood renewal have the potential to improve people's health and well-being. But are there still some people left out? Right back in Activity 3, Dave Kellett referred to the people who were isolated and excluded. They have not been much in evidence in this unit. In Unit 10, you will be thinking about the people in Thornhill who are 'hard to reach', and finding out what Thornhill Plus You has to offer them.

End-of-unit checklist

Studying this unit should have helped you to:

- explain the concept of a healthy neighbourhood, and how a neighbourhood's resources – or lack of them – affect people's health and well-being
- discuss some ways in which where people live has an impact on their health
- understand the implications of poverty and social exclusion for health and well-being
- understand the concept of neighbourhood renewal, and how it can help to improve health
- discuss the advantages and challenges of involving local people in improving health and well-being.

References

Benjamin, A. (2006) 'Poverty isn't always easy to recognise', *Guardian*, *Society*, 8 November, p. 4; also available online at www.guardian.co.uk/society/2006/nov/08/socialexclusion.comment/print (Accessed 3 March 2008).

Botting, B. (ed.) (1995) *The Health of Our Children*, Decennial Supplement Series DS no. 11, London, HMSO.

Bowers, H., Macadam, A., Patel, M. and Smith, C. (2006) *Making a Difference through Volunteering*, London, CSV; also available online at www.csv.org.uk/NR/rdonlyres/7B94D859-9403-4B2E-9E96-07238F167034/42888/MakingaDifferenceThroughVolunteeringOlderPeopleCar.pdf (Accessed 3 March 2008).

Carr-Hill, R. (1990) 'The measurement of inequalities in health: lessons from the British experience', *Social Science and Medicine*, vol. 31, no. 3, pp. 393–404.

Centre for Public Policy and Management, Robert Gordon University (undated) *An Introduction to Social Policy* [online], www2.rgu.ac.uk/publicpolicy/introduction/needf.htm (Accessed 3 March 2008).

Coates, D. (2005) *Prolonged Labour: The Slow Birth of New Labour Britain*, Basingstoke, Palgrave Macmillan.

CSV (2005) *The Great British Time Survey* [online], www.csv.org.uk/News/Time+Survey.htm (Accessed 3 March 2008).

Department for Work and Pensions (DWP) (2006) *Opportunity For All: Eighth Annual Report 2006* [online], www.dwp.gov.uk/ofa/reports/2006/pdf/StrategyandIndicators-FullReport.pdf (Accessed 3 March 2008).

Dinham, A. (2005) 'Empowered or over-powered? The real experiences of local participation in the UK's New Deal for Communities', *Community Development Journal*, vol. 40, no. 3, pp. 301–12.

Dinham, A. (2006) 'Raising expectations or dashing hopes? Well-being and participation in disadvantaged areas', *Community Development Journal* Advance Access, 12 January, pp. 1–13.

Disability Rights Commission (2007) *Equal Treatment: Closing the Gap. A Formal Investigation into Physical Health Inequalities Experienced by People with Learning Disabilities and/or Mental Health Problems* [online], www.equalityhumanrights.com/Documents/Disability/Formal%20investigations/DRC%20Health%20Formal%20Investigation%20main%20report%20part%201.doc (Accessed 30 September 2007).

Gowman, N. (1999) *Healthy Neighbourhoods*, London, King's Fund; also available online at www.kingsfund.org.uk/publications/kings_fund_publications/healthy.html (Accessed 2 March 2008).

Hashagen, S. (2003) 'Frameworks for measuring community health and well being' in Orme, J., Powell, J., Taylor, P., Harrison, T. and Grey, M. (eds) *Public Health Policy for the 21st Century: New Perspectives on Policy, Participation and Practice*, Maidenhead, Open University Press.

Independent Inquiry into Inequalities in Health (1998) *Independent Inquiry into Inequalities in Health: Report* (Acheson Report), Chaired by Sir Donald Acheson, London, The Stationery Office [online], www.archive.official-documents.co.uk/document/doh/ih/part1a.htm (Accessed 2 March 2008).

Knight, J. (2005) 'The changing face of poverty', BBC News, 26 July [online], http://news.bbc.co.uk/go/pr/fr/-/1/hi/business/4070112.stm (Accessed 3 March 2008).

National Statistics (undated) *Neighbourhood Statistics* [online], www.neighbourhood. statistics.gov.uk/dissemination/NeighbourhoodSummary.do?a=3& c=SO19+6PB& g=411922& i=1001x1012x1013& j=301536& m=1& p=2& q=1& w1=1024& enc=1& tab=1& inWales=false&width=1024 (Accessed 3 March 2008).

New Policy Institute (undated(a)) *Notes: Choices of Low Income Threshold* [online], www.poverty.org.uk/summary/income%20intro.shtml (Accessed 3 March 2008).

New Policy Institute (undated(b)) *Scotland: Premature Death* [online], www.poverty.org. uk/S35/index.shtml (Accessed 3 March 2008).

New Policy Institute (undated(c)) *Summary: What the Indicators Show: Health* [online], www.poverty.org.uk/summary/health.htm (Accessed 3 March 2008).

New Policy Institute (undated(d)) *United Kingdom: Low Birthweight Babies* [online], www.poverty.org.uk/11/index.shtml?2 (Accessed 3 March 2008).

New Policy Institute (undated(e)) *United Kingdom: Mental Health* [online], www.poverty.org.uk/37/index.shtml?2 (Accessed 3 March 2008).

New Policy Institute (undated(f)) *United Kingdom: Premature Death* [online], http://www.poverty.org.uk/35/index.shtml?2 (Accessed 19 June 2008).

NHS Confederation (2007) *About Primary Care Trusts* [online], www.nhsconfed.org/ primary-care-trusts/primary-care-tr-1762.cfm (Accessed 3 March 2008).

NHS Direct (2008) *What Are Primary Care Trusts (PCTs)?* [online], www.nhsdirect.nhs. uk/articles/article.aspx?articleId=1078# (Accessed 3 March 2008).

NHS Health Scotland (2003) *Insight: Case Studies in Community Development and Health in Scotland*, Edinburgh, NHS Health Scotland; also available online at www.healthscotland.com/uploads/documents/InsightBook.pdf (Accessed 15 May 2008).

Office of the Deputy Prime Minister (2003) *Factsheet 9: New Deal for Communities*, Office of the Deputy Prime Minister, Neighbourhood Renewal Unit [online], www.neighbourhood.gov.uk/publications.asp?did=159 (Accessed 3 March 2008).

Palmer, G., MacInnes, T. and Kenway, P. (2007) *Monitoring Poverty and Social Exclusion 2007*, York, Joseph Rowntree Foundation.

Quilgars, D. (2004) *Communities Caring and Developing: Lessons from Hull*, York, Joseph Rowntree Foundation.

Secretary of State for Health (1999) *Saving Lives: Our Healthier Nation*, Cm 4386, London, The Stationery Office; also available online at www.archive.official-documents.co.uk/document/cm43/4386/4386-sm.htm (Accessed 2 March 2008).

Snaith, R. (1989) *Neighbourhood Care and Social Policy*, London, HMSO.

Social Exclusion Taskforce (2006) *What Is Social Exclusion?* [online], http://archive. cabinetoffice.gov.uk/seu/pageac0b.html?id=96&pId=27&url=page.asp?id=213 (Accessed 3 March 2008).

Social Exclusion Unit (2001) *A Commitment to Neighbourhood Renewal: National Strategy Action Plan*, London, Social Exclusion Unit/Cabinet Office; also available online at www.neighbourhood.gov.uk/publications.asp?did=85 (Accessed 15 May 2008).

Southampton Online (2007) *Deprivation* [online], www.southampton.gov.uk/thecouncil/ thecity/research/IMD2004/indexofdeprivation.asp (Accessed 3 March 2008).

Spencer, N. (1996) *Poverty and Child Health*, Oxford, Radcliffe Medical Press.

Spicker, P. (1993) *Poverty and Social Security*, London, Routledge.

Spicker, P. (2007) *The Idea of Poverty*, Bristol, The Policy Press.

Taylor, P. (2003) 'The lay contribution to public health' in Orme, J., Powell, J., Taylor, P., Harrison, T. and Grey, M. (eds) *Public Health Policy for the 21st Century: New Perspectives on Policy, Participation and Practice*, Maidenhead, Open University Press.

Thomas, A., Pettigrew, N., Cotton, D. and Tovey, P. (1999) *Keeping in Touch with the Labour Market: A Qualitative Evaluation of the Back to Work Bonus*, London, Department for Work and Pensions; also available online at www.dwp.gov.uk/asd/asd5/96summ.asp (Accessed 3 March 2008).

Thornhill Plus You (undated) *Looking Ahead: Delivery Plan 2005–2011* [online], www.thornhillplusyou.co.uk/lookingahead.asp (Accessed 3 March 2008).

Working Group on Inequalities in Health (1980) *Inequalities in Health: Report of a Research Working Group* (The Black Report), Chaired by Sir Douglas Black, London, Department of Health and Social Security.

World Health Organization (WHO) (1946) *Preamble to the Constitution of the World Health Organization as Adopted by the International Health Conference, New York, 19 June – 22 July 1946* [online], www.who.int/suggestions/faq/en (Accessed 26 February 2008).

WRVS (2007), *WRVS Action*, issue 31, autumn [online], www.wrvs.org.uk/DocUploads/ACTION31_191007.pdf (Accessed 3 March 2008).

Yeandle, S., Escott, K., Grant, L. and Batty, E. (2003) *Women and Men Talking about Poverty*, Manchester, Equal Opportunities Commission.

Website

www.avon.nhs.uk/phnet/PHinfo/understanding.htm (Accessed 3 March 2008).

Unit 10

Inclusion and exclusion in the community

Prepared for the course team by Fran Wiles

Contents

Introduction

> I love my neighbourhood. Not every neighbourhood's the same, admittedly. But in my neighbourhood, they are very very caring, and very friendly.
>
> (Pauline Vaughan, Thornhill resident, DVD, Block 3, Unit 9, Activity 5 video)

Despite the efforts of neighbourhood renewal projects like Thornhill Plus You, some people don't experience communities as supportive and inclusive places. In Unit 9, you saw that neighbourhood-based services not only improve people's health and well-being, but also help to foster a sense of belonging and ownership among people who live there. But how likely are these services to be used by people who don't feel part of the community?

Unit 10 considers whether a community approach to health and social care can meet the needs of people who are excluded or isolated. You will continue to draw on the Thornhill case study, exploring people's different experiences of their neighbourhood.

The unit considers the importance of social networks, and asks: what happens when people don't have access to supportive social networks? You will be looking at the implications of this, and at what care services can do to bridge the gap.

Finally, this unit takes a brief look back at the effectiveness of neighbourhood renewal and community-based provision.

Core questions

- How can communities support people?
- Why do isolated and excluded people sometimes avoid using care services?
- Can community-based services offer anything to people who are excluded and on the margins of society?
- Can neighbourhood renewal be effective in the longer term?

Are you taking the IVR?

If you are studying K101 as part of the Integrated Vocational Route (IVR), don't forget to check your VQ Candidate Handbook to see which Unit 10 activities contribute to your electronic portfolio.

1 Different experiences of 'community'

In Block 3 so far, you have been thinking about communities as places where people live, and where they can get support with their health and social care needs. The focus now shifts to community in its broader sense and to some of Thornhill's more specialised health and care services.

1.1 What is a community?

Even when the word 'community' is used to describe a specific place – for example, a neighbourhood – this doesn't necessarily mean that everyone experiences it in the same way. In the next activity, you return to the residents of Thornhill, to explore this idea further.

DVD

Activity 1   Neighbourhoods mean different things to different people

Allow about one hour

You will hear four of the Thornhill residents talking about their neighbourhood: Shelley, a young mother with three children; Alexis, who has learning difficulties; Pauline, a local volunteer who has lived in Thornhill for a long time; and David, who has recently moved into the neighbourhood. You will also be able to see a map showing how each person uses local facilities, and the people with whom they have regular contact.

Find Block 3, Unit 10, Activity 1 on the DVD.

Comment

This activity will have underlined the point that neighbourhoods can mean different things to different people. The way you view your neighbourhood depends on factors such as your age and circumstances, how much time you spend there, your mode of transport, and how long you've lived there.

In Activity 1, you answered four questions:

1   You looked at how far each person's needs are met within the boundary of Thornhill, and how often they leave the estate.

2   You considered what each person *feels* about Thornhill, as a place to live.

3   You made a note about the relationships that were mentioned.

4   You noted what each person did that brought them into regular contact with others.

Your responses will help you to understand the different ways in which the word 'community' can be used, and how each meaning relates to care.

Different kinds of housing in Thornhill (left)

Not all neighbourhoods look like Thornhill. This is Glenluce, a village in south-west Scotland (right)

Locality

The first question in Activity 1 relates to the idea that a community is a place, a locality. The word 'community' is often used by local councils and health organisations to describe a geographical area – for example, a town, a village or a housing estate – and the amenities and services organised around it. In the case of Thornhill, the community is quite a small place: a housing estate, with a boundary that can be mapped out fairly easily.

The Thornhill housing estate was built mainly in the 1950s and 1960s. It was part of a massive national rebuilding programme which had begun in the 1930s, demolishing old slum housing in the inner cities and replacing it with modern estates on the outskirts of towns. The programme was suspended during the Second World War, but thereafter it was stepped up to deal with the consequences of bomb damage. During the 1950s and 1960s, the effects of breaking up long-standing communities became an issue of interest to sociologists. A famous study of Bethnal Green, a traditional working-class community in East London, observed that people's lives at that time revolved around a close web of family members living in the same neighbourhood. Family life, work and leisure all took place here, so that ties with family, friends and neighbours were continually reinforced from day to day (Young and Willmott, 1957). Despite the problems of poverty and dilapidated, inadequate housing, Bethnal Green residents valued this way of life because of its supportive relationships and 'community spirit'. Today, by contrast, families tend to be more dispersed; for example, you might recall that in Unit 9, Activity 5, Cheree and Rachel mentioned relatives living in other parts of Southampton; and Jill told how her children had moved away from the estate as soon as they were old enough to do so.

From the 1930s, much of the older housing in the inner cities was replaced by modern council housing estates

The second question – what people feel about Thornhill – will have highlighted an important aspect of communities which relates to the idea of locality: this is a sense of belonging or attachment (Stacey, 1969) which unites people. In Unit 5, you considered the concept of attachment in relation to significant others. However, people can also develop an attachment to a place, often to where they grew up or live currently.

Social networks

The third and fourth questions refer to people's relationships. This suggests another way of thinking about the concept of community, which has less to do with its physical dimensions and more to do with the connections between people. Sociologists call these sets of relationships – between friends, neighbours, work colleagues, family members – 'social networks'. In the Bethnal Green community, these networks acted as a vital source of mutual support. Before the introduction of the NHS, welfare benefits and social services, working-class people had no choice but to rely on each other for support, through times of poverty, ill health and unemployment (Roberts, 1984). And although social networks are less vital to daily life nowadays, they continue to be linked with the idea of support.

Communities of identity

In addition to locality and social networks, there is a third way of understanding community. In Activity 1, David describes himself as 'a man of faith' because he is a practising Christian. As well as feeling connected to Thornhill, David also belongs to the Christian community: a community which depends neither on locality nor on a social network, but on a shared sense of identity, based on common beliefs. Sociologist Peter Willmott suggests that a community of identity can draw on a wide range of interests:

[*In this context, propinquity means 'closeness' or 'similarity in nature'.]

> … the word [community] can refer to … people who share in common something other than physical propinquity[*] … what is shared may cover things as diverse as ethnic origin, religion, politics, occupation, leisure pursuit and sexual propensity.

(Willmott, 1984, pp. 4–5)

Irish Travellers: a community based on shared identity

Activity 2   Belonging to a community

Allow about 10 minutes

(a) Think of two communities that you feel part of. Jot down a few notes to explain which of the following meanings describes them best:

- a community based on locality
- a community based on relationships between people who know each other
- a community based on shared identity.

(b) How do these communities provide you with support, in terms of social, emotional and physical well-being?

Comment

Here are some of the course testers' responses:

- I don't feel part of my neighbourhood, having only lived here for a short time. I'm still registered with my old GP and go to a dentist near my workplace. At work I do feel part of an identity community and this gives me a kind of emotional support.

- I'm connected to other people through email – I keep in regular contact with family and friends who live far away. We keep in touch with each other's lives and share advice about children, health and so on.

- I feel strongly connected to my neighbourhood and spend most of my time here. I have friends who live nearby, and am in a babysitting circle with other parents around here. If I feel lonely and miserable I just take the baby out in the buggy. It makes me feel good when people recognise me and are prepared to stop for a chat.

- I belong to an online community, as I'm in an internet support group. I log on every day and tell people about problems I'm having, see how they're getting on, and generally chat about everyday things like what we watched on TV last night.

Telephones, mobile phones and the internet have made it easier to maintain a sense of community across long distance. In Unit 6 you saw that this makes it possible to offer support to others, even if they don't live close by.

Summing up, then, the word 'community' can be understood in three different ways, to describe:

- a community based on locality
- a community based on the relationships between people who know each other
- a community based on shared identity.

These meanings are not mutually exclusive and often overlap. People can belong to several different communities at the same time. Shelley and Pauline talk about their strong sense of belonging to Thornhill as a place. At the same time, they have supportive social networks arising from the activities they take part in (Cooking Pots, t'ai chi) and their relationships with others in the neighbourhood. When David attends the local church, he feels a sense of belonging with others who share his faith. At the same time, he is developing relationships with people who live in his neighbourhood.

A common thread underpins all three meanings of community: the sense of belonging which brings people together. Feeling connected to any kind of community provides people with a feeling of security and a source of identity: a sense of where they come from and who they are. However, not everyone who lives in the same locality shares this sense of belonging, and not all communities are experienced positively.

1.2 Social networks and support

As you saw in Activity 2, different kinds of community offer different kinds of support. The Thornhill Plus You activities that you explored in Unit 9 offered a mixture of informal and formal support which was organised around a neighbourhood. Social networks, on the other hand, are a source of support that is not necessarily linked with where people live.

To find out what support was offered by people's social networks, researchers Chris Phillipson and his colleagues used a method developed by Kahn and Antonucci (cited in Phillipson et al., 2001, p. 29). They began by asking participants to identify others who were important to them, and to mark these relationships on a diagram, according to how significant they were. You can see an example of such a diagram in Figure 1, based loosely on what Shelley said about her social network in Activity 1. In the film, Shelley mentioned her partner, her three children, her father, her partner's parents, and her friend. There are probably lots of other people she didn't talk about – for instance, she may know other parents through attending toddler groups and the Cooking Pots sessions at the Natterbox.

Phillipson and colleagues explain how they asked people to fill in the diagram. To begin with, the word 'you' is written in the centre, and then:

> Respondents are asked to place in the inner circle those persons who are 'so close and important' that they 'cannot imagine life without them'. Those considered less close but still important are listed in the middle and outer circles.

(Phillipson et al., 2001, p. 29)

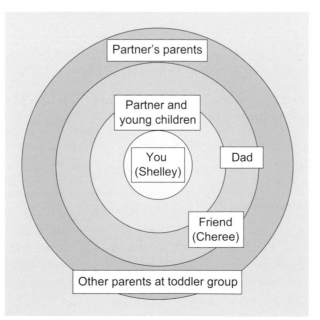

Figure 1 An example of a network diagram, based on one used by Phillipson et al. (2001, p. 266)

A social network, then, consists of 'the set of people with whom one maintains contact and has some form of social bond' (Bowling et al., quoted in Phillipson et al., 2001, p. 26). Within a social network, relationships vary in nature and significance. Using a system of circles to map out someone's social network, it is possible to see both the number of relationships involved, and the different degrees of importance that a person attaches to each one. Shelley wasn't asked any details about her relationships with others, so the diagram is partly fictional. I have filled in the diagram as if the people she feels closest to are her partner and her children. I've put her father and her best friend (let's imagine this is Cheree) in the next circle – nearly as close and important as Shelley's partner. For the purpose of this example, I've placed her partner's parents, and the people she knows from the toddler group, in the outer circle: as if these people are important to Shelley but less close.

Social networks are an important aspect of community life because, as you have seen throughout the course so far, a great deal of care and support is provided informally within families and, to some extent, within friendship groups. In Phillipson et al.'s research, once the participants had indicated the extent of their social networks, they were asked to elaborate on the 'variety of support functions that network members provide or receive' (Phillipson et al., 2001, p. 29). Phillipson et al. were researching the support needs of older people, and in this context they took support to involve a wide variety of activities, including practical, emotional or financial help. They suggested that practical support includes shopping, help with household chores and other similar tasks. In Shelley's case, it might include babysitting. Financial help varies from offering advice, lending money or paying towards someone's living costs. With regard to the emotional aspects of support, Phillipson et al. cite Kahn and Antonucci's examples:

> ... confiding about things that are important; being reassured when feeling uncertain; being respected; talking with someone when upset, nervous or depressed; talking with someone about their health ...

> (Phillipson et al., 2001, p. 30)

Finding out about someone's social networks is a useful way to identify actual or potential sources of support available to that individual. It can also show relationships in which support or care is provided on a reciprocal basis. Shelley looks after her three young children, but it's likely that in her other relationships there is a degree of mutual support. For example, Shelley and her friend might look after each other's children in an emergency. Supposing one of them is going through a difficult time – a toddler who doesn't sleep well, for example – they can talk about the stresses and anxieties of parenting. If Shelley's dad were to get flu, she might collect his prescription and do some shopping for him. Perhaps he would babysit when Shelley and her partner wanted a night out.

In the next activity you consider the variation in people's social networks and the resources they offer.

Activity 3   Mapping social networks

Allow about 30 minutes

(a) Think about the different experiences you considered in Activity 1. Using this information, draw network diagrams (based on Figure 1) for:

- Pauline
- Alexis
- yourself or, if relevant, someone you know through your work.

(b) What kind of help might each person's social network be able to offer:

- on a day-to-day basis?

- now and again?

- in an emergency?

  Do you think this help is likely to be reciprocal?

Comment

Pauline. Perhaps you placed Pauline's best friend Elaine in the inner circle of her social network, and her neighbours in one of the outer circles?

Elaine, in particular, is a day-to-day source of emotional support for Pauline. Her neighbours would probably be able to provide practical help now and again. It sounds as if they would help Pauline in an emergency, and in this kind of situation could be on the spot more quickly than Elaine. You might have included the people Pauline works with at the Thornhill Health and Wellbeing Network, and the people she meets at t'ai chi – it would be reasonable to think that they provide a certain amount of emotional support, and perhaps health care advice.

Pauline is close to Elaine, and very active as a volunteer, so she will almost certainly offer reciprocal support to her friends and neighbours.

Alexis. The most significant person in Alexis' network appears to be his brother, Philip. Philip describes himself as Alexis' carer, and provides practical, emotional and financial support. In the film, Alexis mentions only his neighbours: he describes them as 'fine'. It's not clear whether this means simply that they don't give him any trouble, or that they actually talk to each other. Bowling et al.'s definition of social networks includes only people with whom you have ongoing contact and some form of bond or connection (cited in Phillipson et al., 2001, p. 26). It's possible that this includes Alexis' neighbours – someone who tested K101 placed them in the outer circle of his social network, and thought they might be called on, but only in an emergency.

You might have included the people at the Eastpoint Community Centre in Alexis' social network. He seems to attend groups or advice sessions there, which would provide practical and emotional support (possibly mutual). Finally, Alexis is a voluntary worker with the Red Cross. He is engaged in helping others, and probably gets companionship and emotional support from his fellow volunteers, so this is part of his network.

Although social networks can be a source of support, Activity 3 shows that people's networks vary, both in size and in the extent to which they can be relied on for different kinds of help. Alexis – as far as we can tell – has fewer sources of support than Pauline, and most of his support seems to come from just one person: his brother Philip.

Not everyone in a social network is able or willing to provide support (Phillipson et al., 2001, p. 30). And having a large social network doesn't always mean that support is at hand, but it does offer some flexibility. If one person can't help, there may be someone else who can be approached. However, having a small network reduces the number of people who can be called on for assistance. As Pearlin points out:

> People are not likely to reach out at any one time to all the resources encompassed by their networks; on the other hand, they are certainly not able to call on more resources than are provided by their network.

(Pearlin, quoted in Phillipson et al., 2001, p. 26)

You be a good pussy for the nice man, Kitty, whilst I'm away having my cataracts done.

Social networks – which can include neighbours and friends – can be a source of support when help is needed

Social networks and the nature of relationships change over time. For example, parents of young children usually have regular contact with each other, through parent–toddler groups and informal gatherings at the school gates. This makes it easier to develop mutually supportive networks. By the time children are entering their teens, however, they are becoming more independent, and many parents report feeling isolated (Edwards, 2004). During their working lives, people may not spend enough time in their neighbourhoods to develop local networks (Harris and Gale, 2004).

So far, then, you have seen that social networks are an important source of support for people in everyday life. In most cases, this kind of informal support is reciprocal. However, people's social networks vary in their capacity to be supportive: some people can call on a large or very reliable pool of help, while others have fewer resources to draw on. Social networks change over time, and maintaining them takes a certain amount of effort and skill.

1.3 Helping people to develop social networks

In the next activity, you will be reading about an innovative service which helped older people to develop and maintain social networks in their own neighbourhoods and communities, after being discharged from hospital. The authors argue that supporting such social networks is important because after a period in hospital, people have difficulty adjusting to life back at home:

> Sustaining recovery and the routines of home life ... can make heavy demands on service users' psychological resources, particularly when living alone and experiencing multiple health problems or impairments ...

(Resource 8, p. 43)

The service you are going to read about was provided by Age Concern, a voluntary organisation. Nearly all the people using the service lived alone, and had long-term health conditions. The aim of the scheme was to help people to access social networks that would enable them to resume their lives in the community, stay in good health, and avoid having to move into residential care. The scheme was interested in supporting people's social networks in the widest possible sense: not just with friends, family and neighbours, but also in essential day-to-day encounters with shops, banks and social care professionals.

Activity 4   Supporting vulnerable people's networks

Allow about one hour

Resources

Read Resource 8, 'For the sake of their health: older service users' requirements for social care to facilitate access to social networks', by Eileen McLeod, Paul Bywaters, Denise Tanner and Maureen Hirsch. As you do so:

(a) Note down two examples of social networks that people were helped to maintain or develop as a result of the service.

(b) In each case, make a few notes about what might have happened to the service user without this support.

Comment

Examples include:

- A man being able to keep up his hobby, fishing, and the social life which revolved around it. This enabled him to pursue a pastime he enjoyed. Without this support, he would have become demoralised and isolated, and his well-being would have been reduced.

- A woman who found it hard to pay her bills because of hearing and cognitive impairments being supported to discuss this with her bank manager. If she hadn't had this help, her bills would probably have remained unpaid, which would cause her a lot of anxiety. She would have had financial problems and might have lost important services. This could have put her independence at risk, if other people felt that she was no longer able to live alone.

- A woman being helped to relearn how to use a telephone, so that she could keep in contact with friends and her local shop. This enabled her to stay independent and to retain control over her day-to-day life. Without this support, she would have been dependent on other people to do her shopping for her. She would also have lost contact with her friends – a source of well-being and support.

From this reading, you can see that social networks provide an important resource to help people regain their physical, social and emotional well-being after a period of illness. The problem is that people in such situations as those you have just read about – needing help with day-to-day living after being discharged from hospital – can find it especially difficult to maintain social networks, because they have lost confidence and self-esteem. The people in the study by Eileen McLeod and her colleagues also lacked certain skills required for keeping in contact with others. In Unit 9, you came across people of all ages enjoying a range of neighbourhood activities, such as t'ai chi, the tea dance, Crafty Crafters and the THAWP drop-in sessions. Do you think that any of the people you have just read about would have gone along to these activities by themselves? Even if they were interested, it seems probable that – without support – the difficulty of getting around, and their lack of confidence, would have made it unlikely.

Thornhill's tea dances are an enjoyable and important source of social contact for older residents, some of whom live alone

Social networks need not be confined to family, friends and neighbours. When people don't have supportive personal networks, care workers can step in, not only to provide hands-on help, but also to put them in touch with other sources of help. Indeed, care workers sometimes become part of people's networks. In Resource 8, McLeod et al. write that the older people in their study came to see the Age Concern workers as friends. Think back to the Somebody Cares home care agency in Unit 3: the service users would almost certainly include their regular home care workers in their social networks (although the staff themselves were careful to maintain professional boundaries).

Without the support of the Age Concern workers, the people you read about might not have managed to remain living at home as they wished to do. However, supportive social networks appear to have benefits for people's physical well-being too. As you read in Resource 8, researchers have discovered that having supportive networks is associated with a number of health benefits: for example, it helps to lower blood pressure and maintain cognitive functioning. People who have support from others are also known to be more resilient in a psychological sense, which helps them to cope with the demands of long-term ill health and impairment. Some studies have even suggested a link between social networks and life expectancy. Robert Putnam, an American sociologist, argues that:

> As a rule of thumb, if you belong to no groups but decide to join one, you cut your risk of dying over the next year in half. If you smoke and belong to no groups, it's a toss-up statistically whether you should stop smoking or start joining.

(Putnam, 2000, p. 331)

Being part of a social network is good for your health

To support this view, Putnam (2000) cites a number of research studies which indicate that people with a high number of social contacts – through marriage, close relationships with friends and relatives, and membership of religious and other organisations – are likely to live longer than people who are poorly integrated into social networks. In talking about social networks, Putnam includes organised groups, in addition to those that arise spontaneously from everyday social contacts. You looked at groups in Unit 6, and will be coming back to them again in the next section.

In this section you have seen that communities can be a source of social networks, and that these have the potential to provide significant support. People who have good social networks are healthier too. However, vulnerable or disadvantaged people may lack the means to develop supportive networks. This is where care services can fill the gap.

Key points

- The word 'community' has several meanings, which have in common a sense of belonging to place, people or shared identity.

- Social networks can be a valuable resource for health, well-being and support, but people's networks vary in their capacity to be supportive.

- Some people who are isolated and vulnerable need help from care services to maintain and develop supportive social networks.

Reader

Learning skills: Keeping up your concentration

Do you feel you are settling into a rhythm of studying now? Are you managing to avoid the kind of bitty, distracted sessions you read about in Zahra's case on pages 14 and 15 of *The Good Study Guide*? Have you got over the urge to make a cup of tea as soon as you have seated yourself, or to tidy your shelves? Of course, there are reasons why it is so easy to be distracted when you study – look back quickly at the quotation from the student on page 39 of *The Good Study Guide* and the box just below it.

So if all these things can distract you, what can help you to concentrate? Think back over your best s`essions of study. When have you concentrated particularly well? Was it when you:

- had set yourself a clear target?
- switched regularly from one task to another?
- made a point of scanning ahead so that you knew what you were reading about?
- were fresh from a nap?
- were really interested in the topic?

Or was it other kinds of things which kept you focused? The more insight you have into your own motivation, capabilities and habits of thought, the better you can play to your strengths. Don't feel that you have to study according to some universal formula. There isn't one. Make up your own.

2 Supporting people to access community resources for health and social care

The health and well-being activities that you looked at in Unit 9 were built around local priorities and needs: they were accessible and open to everyone in the neighbourhood. But what if you don't have the confidence to step over the threshold of the Centre for Healthy Living or the Natterbox Community Centre? What if you feel too much of an outsider to risk joining in? What if you haven't even heard of these facilities?

In this section, you will be looking at two community-based services designed for people with particular support needs. Like the Age Concern scheme you read about in the previous section, Thornhill Family Support and the Family Support Service in Tower Hamlets are not open to everyone: they are available only to people who meet specific criteria.

2.1 Family support services

The case study in the next activity is based on a real situation. It's the story of Mina Ali (not her real name). Let's suppose that the local authority has recently allocated Mina and her partner, Karim Ali, a small flat in Thornhill, perhaps in one of the tower blocks or walk-up blocks.

Activity 5   No one to turn to
Allow about 10 minutes

Read the short case study below, and then jot down your answer to the question that follows.

Mina Ali (Part 1)

Mina Ali, a Bangladeshi woman in her thirties, is pregnant with her third child, but has missed most of her antenatal appointments. The community midwife notes from Mina's medical history that she has been diagnosed as suffering from moderate depression.

She visits Mina and finds her withdrawn and barely able to talk. Her partner has stayed home from work for the midwife's visit, because Mina doesn't speak much English. As the midwife is unable to speak their language (Bengali), he acts as an interpreter. He says that Mina is tired all the time and seems unable to leave the flat. She is having difficulty in looking after their two young children (one aged twelve months, the other aged two) while Karim is at work. Through her partner, Mina acknowledges this and also indicates that she is suffering from pain in her back and neck.

Karim explains that they haven't lived here long, and their only relatives in this country live 200 miles away. He says that they don't speak to their neighbours.

(Adapted from Gray, 2003)

Look at Figure 2, which represents Mina's social networks. What does this suggest about the kind of support available to her?

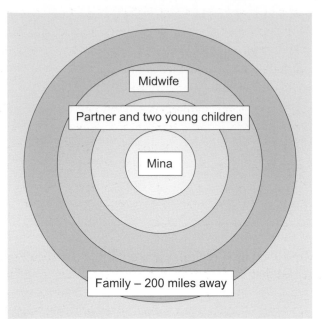

Figure 2   Diagram of Mina Ali's social network

Comment

The network diagram in Figure 2 shows that – apart from her partner who is working during the day – Mina has very few people to call on for help. There are some statutory services – the midwife, for example. The midwife might be able to put the family in contact with other services. There are family members living at a distance – they can't be called on for practical help, but may be able to offer some emotional support by phone (if they have one). The neighbours are not included in the diagram because Mina has no ongoing contact or connection with them. However, it's possible they might be called on in an emergency.

In Unit 9, you saw pregnant women and mothers with babies and toddlers enjoying each other's company and support in a number of local activities. And as you saw in Unit 6, people can gain considerable support from coming together in self help groups. You will recall that Anna Clarke, the health visitor, organised a range of groups as part of her health promotion work. So what facilities might Mina find in Thornhill to help her?

Activity 6   Would Mina join any neighbourhood groups?

Allow about 20 minutes

Resources

Read Resource 9, 'Activities and groups in Thornhill'. Many of the activities and groups described there will be familiar to you already.

(a) Imagine that Mina lives in Thornhill. Look at the list of activities and read the descriptions. Mark any that you think would be of benefit to her, and make a note to say why.

(b) What might prevent Mina from taking part in these activities?

Comment

(a) Lots of the activities are potentially useful: the community midwives' sessions, and the various activities for the under-5s. These would give Mina a chance to sit down and relax while her children played safely. She would meet other parents in similar circumstances. You might also have noted the various drop-in sessions, where both Mina and her partner could get advice about housing or health concerns.

(b) However, Mina is feeling very tired and unwell, and there is also the difficulty of speaking very little English. It seems unlikely that she will take the step of leaving her flat – accompanied by two small children – to seek out unfamiliar people and activities. She may not know where the groups take place. She might also feel shy or wary about joining in activities with people whose culture and language are different from her own.

If Mina lived in Thornhill, she would find it difficult to join in the community activities that Shelley, Rachel and Cheree have found so useful. Poor physical (and perhaps mental) health makes it hard for her to actively seek out and join groups. She may not even know what's available, especially if there is no information in Bengali. And, as you saw in Unit 6, it can be difficult for people to join groups when they don't share the culture and language of other members.

However, a service that she might find helpful is Thornhill Family Support. This is a specialised service for families who need more help than they would get from attending drop-in groups. You heard briefly about this in Unit 9, Activity 11, and will find more information in Resource 10, 'Thornhill Family Support'.

Activity 7 Support from a peer

Allow about 25 minutes

Resources

Read Resource 10, 'Thornhill Family Support'. What do you think the advantages of this service would be for Mina? Are there likely to be any difficulties?

Comment

Mina would get a friendly approach from someone who has experience of living locally and bringing up children. The support worker would be able to go with Mina to appointments, and provide practical support in the home.

However, someone who tested this activity said: 'The service may or may not benefit Mina – it depends on how culturally sensitive the workers are.' Would Mina be able to have a support worker who speaks Bengali? If not, communication would be difficult. As Mina is from Bangladesh (and is Muslim), she might prefer to have a worker who understands her culture and religion. Would the support workers be sensitive to these?

One of the distinct advantages of Thornhill Family Support is being able to get support from a peer – someone who has shared the same experiences and hardships, someone to 'hold your hand' when you lack the confidence or know-how to access services. As you read in Resource 10, the Locality Family Workers are recruited from the neighbourhood and have similar backgrounds and experiences to the families they support. While the predominantly white English workers in Thornhill would probably be able to establish enough common ground and trust with Mina to help her overcome some of her difficulties, other areas may be more challenging. You will remember from Unit 2 that Anwar Malik found it difficult to follow his diabetic diet until it was tailored to his cultural needs. Mina and her family might have particular cultural needs; for example, to do with pregnancy, childcare and food.

The real 'Mina', on whom this case study is based, lived not in Thornhill but in the London Borough of Tower Hamlets. She is one of thirty families who took part in a research study about a voluntary agency provision called the Family Support Service (FSS). Read what the researcher, Ben Gray, tells us about this part of London:

[*This was the most recent census information available at the time Gray wrote the report, but the 2001 census reveals a similar pattern (Tower Hamlets Council, undated).]

> Tower Hamlets [is one of] ... the ... most deprived boroughs in the United Kingdom (ELCHA, 1995). According to the 1991 census,[*] Tower Hamlets is a multi-ethnic borough, with low levels of home ownership, problems of overcrowding and high unemployment. The non-white population is 36.6 per cent, with a high proportion of Bangladeshis, reaching 60.7 per cent of the population in Spitalfields, where the Family Support Service is based ... Nazroo (1997) found that Bangladeshi and Pakistani people are some of the poorest in Britain and are 50 per cent more likely to suffer from poor health than the majority population.

(Gray, 2003, pp. 363–4)

A Bangladeshi family at home in Tower Hamlets, London

Gray reports that, like Thornhill Family Support, the Tower Hamlets service makes a point of recruiting workers from the local community who understand the views, problems and difficulties that are experienced by families:

> The selection of staff to work in the FSS is specifically aimed at gaining representation from local communities or from those with similar backgrounds to the client group. There are therefore many Family Support Workers (FSWs) from the Bangladeshi community, several white workers, and a Somali worker ... The majority of FSWs are women who work in a ... part-time role.

(Gray, 2003, p. 364)

Both schemes offer practical help to families who have been referred by health visitors or social workers, where there are concerns about a family's ability to provide day-to-day parenting. Like the Thornhill scheme, the Family Support Service in Tower Hamlets provides help with basic tasks such as 'shopping; … contacting other health and social services and obtaining benefits; dealing with … banks; making applications for housing; bill paying; hygiene; cooking for healthy diets and the well-being of children' (Gray, 2003, p. 367).

At the same time, the support workers act as a bridge between isolated families and other services. The Locality Family Workers in Thornhill arrange for families to use community resources such as the Cooking Pots group, which brings parents together in an informal manner and helps them to eat healthily on a low budget. They would also be able to accompany parents, if required, to facilities such as the debt advice and credit union sessions held in the Natterbox Community Centre.

An additional consideration for the Tower Hamlets service is that a large proportion of the local population is Bangladeshi. Gray observed that by matching workers and families who share the same culture and language, the Family Support Service is able to provide someone who can: 'listen to and understand the family's point of view, then communicate the family's specific health and social care needs to other agencies' (Gray, 2003, p. 375). The Tower Hamlets support workers therefore play 'a very active role with Bangladeshi families in establishing links with the Bangladeshi and wider community' (Gray, 2003, p. 367).

Now that you have a general sense of what the Tower Hamlets Family Support Service does, in the next activity you will be able to find out how the service assisted Mina.

Activity 8   Building support

Allow about 10 minutes

Read Part 2 of the Mina Ali case study, and complete the task that follows.

Mina Ali (Part 2, what happened next)

The community midwife referred Mina Ali to the Family Support Service in Tower Hamlets. She was introduced to Nadia, a Family Support Worker who spoke the same language as Mina. The Family Support Worker got to know Mina and helped her to re-establish some basic day-to-day routines – for example, going out to the local shops and taking her children for health appointments. She encouraged Mina to play with the children at home, and to go out to local play activities. Nadia offered to accompany Mina to her antenatal appointments, and encouraged her to visit the GP about her back and neck pain.

This led to some further hospital appointments to see a specialist, and as Mina didn't want to take the children with her, Nadia arranged childcare. She went with Mina to the hospital, and eventually it emerged that the mental health diagnosis was a misleading and incorrect one. Mina was in fact suffering from a rare and debilitating physical condition, and as a result of the hospital appointments, she was able to receive appropriate treatment. Nadia worked with the medical staff to explain the illness to Mina in Bengali, and she also helped her to contact a support group for people with a similar condition.

(Adapted from Gray, 2003)

Note how Mina's social networks are expanding and, returning to Figure 2, which you looked at in Activity 5, add some more people to the diagram.

Comment

The second part of the case study shows how the Tower Hamlets Family Support Service has helped Mina to access services and facilities in the local community. You can see that Mina is beginning to build up a bigger network of support. As well as her partner and the midwife, she now has Nadia. Nadia provides a lot of day-to-day help, and, in addition, has introduced Mina to a wider social network. Mina is now in contact with specialist health care staff. She is also getting to know people in the local shops, and the other parents at the playgroup. As a result, the neighbourhood probably feels more familiar. Finally, Nadia has introduced Mina to a support group, where she can share anxieties and advice with people who have similar health problems.

Services like Thornhill Family Support and its counterpart in Tower Hamlets are gaining in popularity due to their success in reaching out to excluded families. A national evaluation of the 'On Track' programme (a government-funded project for socially excluded families with children aged from four to twelve) showed that taking support right into people's homes is beneficial:

> Following home visiting, children's behaviour, school attendance and self-esteem had improved. Parents reported that their home management, confidence, family functioning, health and emotional well-being had benefited and they were less stressed. They were better able to manage their children's behaviour and to access help from other services.
>
> (Buchanan, 2007, p. 195)

2.2 Barriers to accessing community-based health and social care services

Providing services is one thing; getting people to use them is another. Zoe Matthews, Health Project Manager with an organisation called Friends, Families and Travellers, tells how she and her colleagues spent six months visiting Gypsy Traveller sites and recruiting volunteers to train as 'health advocates' for other residents:

> We arranged transport and childcare for all course participants who agreed to attend college for the sessions. The Outreach Worker contacted all participants the night before we were due to start the training, despite this nobody came to the first two sessions.
>
> (Friends, Families and Travellers, 2005, p. 6)

As this suggests, sometimes services are there, but the people they are designed for don't take them up. Why is this?

As part of its drive to widen access to health, social care and other public services, the government's Social Exclusion Unit (SEU) examined the factors that discouraged people from using them. They found that there are three broad groups of adults who have 'significantly poorer life chances than the general population': people with low levels of literacy; disabled people and people with long-term health conditions; and people from certain minority ethnic groups (Office of the Deputy Prime Minister, 2005, pp. 3–5).

The SEU reported that:

> Issues of motivation, esteem and confidence were all identified as barriers to accessing services ... One respondent told us: '... Our service users are so used to not being able to access services they often do not even bother trying to.'
>
> Others told us that they or the people they worked with felt 'awkward', 'uncomfortable' or 'intimidated' when accessing services. This can lead to people delaying the use of services or avoiding using them at all.
>
> When people from disadvantaged groups do access services, they often find it hard to interact effectively with members of staff ... One person in our focus groups told us: 'I found it very hard to find out information and to express myself properly to an official person.'
>
> ... People may also feel that they are 'second rate citizens' compared with people working in services.
>
> (ODPM, 2005, pp. 76–7)

The SEU report focused on particular groups of adults, but its findings can be applied to younger people who face similar barriers in seeking help. According to the SEU, disadvantaged people don't always have the confidence to join groups or classes. They find it difficult to use services 'because they are expected to seek them out and have a certain level of literacy and confidence in pursuing what is available' (ODPM, 2005, p. 78). They also fear 'being exposed in front of others or ... letting themselves down' (ODPM, 2005 p. 79).

Activity 9   What prevents disadvantaged people from using care services?

Allow about 10 minutes

Look at the findings of the SEU report again, and use a highlighter or a pen to pick out the main reasons why disadvantaged people may find it difficult to access care services. Add any others that you have noticed from your own experience.

Comment

Compare the reasons you found with those in the list below.

The SEU's findings suggest that the reasons why people don't access care services include:

- They have given up trying, after previous negative experiences of services.
- They have low self-esteem and feel intimidated by care workers, so avoid contact with them.
- They find it difficult to communicate with care workers, and so have trouble in finding out information and explaining their needs.
- They don't like joining groups in case this leaves them feeling exposed in front of other people.
- They lack the skills and confidence to find information, and to pursue options.

Barriers to do with language and literacy can deter people from seeking information and help

These barriers are illustrated in a study of Gypsy Travellers' experiences of using health care, commissioned by the Department of Health. The researchers found that:

> Embarrassment of explaining an inability to read or write was also accompanied by a fear of being identified as a Traveller and was an explanation for avoidance of such situations. This also has implications for reluctance to attend new health care settings until absolutely necessary.

(Van Cleemput et al., 2004, p. 23)

In addition to the practical problems of accessing services while travelling, there were communication difficulties between health workers and Gypsy Travellers. In some cases, the Travellers' extreme anxiety led to 'angry and hostile styles of communication':

> oh that's alright then, 'I'm only a Gypsy, I'll come to you when I'm dead' and I put the phone down on 'em

(Quoted in Van Cleemput et al., 2004, p. 6)

This in turn led to staff 'feeling that Travellers abuse the system and are behaving unreasonably' and thus a cycle of communication breakdown ensues (Van Cleemput et al., 2004, p. 66).

People from minority ethnic groups are reluctant to seek care services when they feel that these will not meet their cultural needs. As you saw in the case of Mina, language is also a barrier for people who don't speak English well. The same applies to some deaf people who lip-read or use sign language. You will read more about culturally sensitive services in Unit 11.

What the SEU report highlights is that social exclusion – arising, for example, from poverty or cultural differences – can make it difficult for people to express their needs, which consequently go unmet. Sometimes a sense of being 'different' (and, by implication, less valued) prevents people from seeking help.

2.3 Addressing social exclusion through targeted services

The community-based services that you looked at in Unit 9 are available for everyone in the neighbourhood. These kinds of services are sometimes described as 'universal': designed for open access by anyone. Universal services also include mainstream health services, schools, libraries, leisure facilities and transport (DH, 2005). In contrast, some services are 'targeted': they are intended for very specific groups of children and adults who have to be 'referred' to the service by a professional, such as a GP, health visitor or social worker.

Universal services work for the majority of people, but they are not always enough. In a large national study of parents living in poor environments, Deborah Ghate and Neal Hazel (2002) talked with people to find out how satisfied they were with local services. Some of the families in the study had significant and multiple problems: severe poverty, serious long-term health conditions, and acute housing difficulties. Ghate and Hazel found that these very disadvantaged families preferred to get support from formal, targeted services rather than from social networks of relatives, friends and neighbourhood groups. They explain:

> This was … because their greater reliance on support of various kinds coupled with their greater vulnerability exposed them more than others to the downsides of informal support. These were the families … that were

least able to engage in the reciprocal give and take of informal ... support relationships. They were also the families with the most to lose, socially speaking, in terms of being exposed to the scrutiny of neighbours and others in the local community.

(Ghate and Hazel, 2002, pp. 255–6)

Ghate and Hazel draw attention to the 'downsides of informal support'. Help provided through people's social networks may come at a price: it requires a measure of reciprocity, and there is no guarantee that other people will not judge you harshly or breach your privacy. Ghate and Hazel conclude that universal services are very valuable, but argue that these should be provided in addition to – not instead of – formal, targeted services:

[Vulnerable parents need] ... formal support services, which can offer help without expecting reciprocation and advice without breaching confidentiality ... The drive to develop better community-based support services ... should not obscure recognition that there are families who, in addition, require special, targeted services.

(Ghate and Hazel, 2002, p. 256)

Publicising family support services in the Thornhill Plus You newsletter

Ideally, the two kinds of service need to be provided alongside each other. Government policy for children and families, 'as set out in [the Green Paper] Every Child Matters, is that targeted support should, wherever possible, be embedded within universal settings' (Every Child Matters, Change for Children, 2006). For example, Thornhill Family Support offers Thornhill parents one-to-one support and also helps them to remain connected with ordinary social networks in the neighbourhood.

You have now looked at three services – the Age Concern project, Thornhill Family Support and the Family Support Service in Tower Hamlets – which differ from the universal provisions discussed in Unit 9, because they are targeted services available only to people who meet specific criteria. Targeted services are an important addition to community-based activities. Yet these initiatives still leave some people out, people who are even 'harder to reach'. In the next section, you will be able to consider how Thornhill is attempting to address this gap in health and social care support.

Key points

- People who are socially excluded find it difficult to access and use care services, and sometimes prefer to avoid them.

- Locally recruited workers offer sensitive 'peer support' to disadvantaged families, and can act as a bridge to other services.

- Community-based 'universal' services are valuable, but some people need help to access them.

- Excluded and vulnerable families and individuals benefit from additional services targeted at their particular needs and circumstances.

3 Outreach and advocacy: including excluded people

Social relationships are part of community life. They enhance people's well-being and can be a source of support. People who are excluded and vulnerable don't always have supportive social networks. They lack the confidence and skills to take up the opportunities offered by neighbourhood renewal and other community projects. You have seen the advantages of providing one-to-one support for particular groups of isolated people: the Age Concern scheme for vulnerable older people, and the family support projects. However, some people don't fit easily into any kind of service, and are consequently even harder to help.

3.1 People on the margins

Some people live in the community, but are not really part of it. The next activity begins to explore this through the case study of Simon. The case study is based on a real situation, but the person's name and some details have been changed. For example, George is a fictional character, and Simon didn't really live on the Thornhill estate, but it will help you to think about his situation if you imagine him there.

Activity 10   What help is there for Simon?

Allow about 15 minutes

Resources

Read the case study and then jot down your ideas in response to the questions that follow.

> ## Simon
>
> George Taylor is worried about Simon.
>
> George, a retired man, does voluntary work in the Natterbox Community Centre. The problem started a couple of months ago, when Simon Jackson, a man in his early twenties, started to hang around outside the community centre. Simon is considered by local people to be (at best) 'eccentric' and (at worst) 'dangerous'. He talks to himself constantly, as if hearing voices. He is 'edgy' and scared around others. Sometimes he gets drunk, and shouts abusively at passers by. Recently, Simon has been coming right into the community centre, sitting down just inside the entrance and muttering agitatedly to himself (or perhaps to the voices in his head). As the centre is often busy with play sessions for mothers and toddlers, this causes concern among the young parents who find Simon a rather threatening presence. About two weeks ago, Simon started to shout at the children, and the community centre staff have asked him to stay away.
>
> George lives in the same block of flats as Simon. He used to chat to Mr Jackson senior, but Mr Jackson died a year ago and Simon now lives alone. He talks to no one, not even to George who has always tried to be friendly. The flat doesn't seem to have any electricity, and the outside is covered in offensive graffiti. The lock on the front door is broken, and Simon has rigged up a complicated series of padlocks and chains for security.

Simon seems to stay in his flat for weeks at a time, but on other occasions he can be seen around the estate, by himself or with the street drinkers near the shopping parade. He has been banned from the shops and the pub, but tends to loiter around the back, looking for food in the dustbins. Simon doesn't appear to be officially known to health or social care services. In fact, George and the other volunteers have noticed that Simon refuses to go near anyone he perceives as an 'authority figure', and will not engage with statutory agencies of any kind.

George is aware that Simon gets picked on and taunted by some of the young people in the area. When last seen a week ago, he had visible cuts and bruises and looked as if he had been beaten up quite badly.

George thinks Simon needs help, but he doesn't know where to start. There are lots of services and activities on the estate, but would any of them be able to help Simon?

(Adapted from Waddell, 2006)

(a) What kind of help do you think Simon needs? Jot down a few examples.

(b) Look back at Resource 9, 'Activities and groups in Thornhill', which you read for Activity 6, and mark any services or groups that might be relevant to Simon's needs. Now make a note of any reasons why these might be difficult for Simon to access.

Comment

(a) Course testers suggested many possible issues with which Simon might need help: housing problems; cleaning up the graffiti; reporting and dealing with harassment. If he has been assaulted, has he reported this to the police? Does he need any medical attention? Does he need to see someone about his mental health? What does he do for money, food, paying his bills? Is he lonely and does he want more social contact? Actually, as one course tester pointed out, it's hard to know what Simon wants without talking with him ... that's part of the problem!

(b) Simon might need some medical help from the Centre for Healthy Living. If he doesn't want to go there, perhaps there is an NHS Walk-in Centre somewhere nearby? The neighbourhood wardens might be able to help Simon to have the graffiti cleaned up. A service like the THAWP drop-in (or even the mental health drop-in) might be a starting point. It's hard to imagine him at an activity like Crafty Crafters – or even t'ai chi, although he might benefit from it. However, it seems most unlikely that Simon would go along to any of the groups or services listed. As he has been banned from the shops and now the community centre, he would probably feel apprehensive about approaching any kind of group. He may be afraid of people being unkind, or think of the leaders as 'authority'.

Simon appears to be unknown to health and social services, and he is too suspicious of 'authorities' to approach them for help. Sometimes people are more trusting of the voluntary sector (ODPM, 2005, p. 43), but the services you read about in the previous section are individually and specifically aimed at certain 'target groups'. Simon isn't in any of these target groups: he isn't an older person who needs support to stay out of hospital; he isn't the parent of a child 'in need' or 'at risk'. He isn't categorised as having a learning difficulty or being mentally ill (although he may actually have an undiagnosed mental health problem). Simon isn't even causing harm to anyone, apart from shouting at them occasionally.

"But what sort of help..?"

Some people's needs are not easy to label

Is Simon socially excluded?

In Unit 9, Activity 3, you may remember that Dave Kellett, Director of Thornhill Plus You, referred to a section of the local population as being isolated and excluded. Simon is isolated and appears to have no family or friends. He is excluded in a quite literal sense from various parts of the local neighbourhood. Like many people who are socially excluded, Simon has a number of different problems, and they are interlinked. For example, he lives in poor housing conditions, he is unemployed, and he probably has a low income. There are questions about his mental health (and in view of his way of life, there might be concerns about his physical health). He may be the victim of crime, and the graffiti and harassment may indicate prejudice against him on the grounds of his mental health.

If Simon really did live in Thornhill, would he express the same warm feelings towards it as Pauline, Jill or David? Everywhere he goes, Simon is ostracised and pushed away. Community – whether in terms of belonging to a place, or the presence of social networks – holds little significance for him.

3.2 Reaching out to people who are excluded

George's dilemma is that Simon appears to need some kind of help, but it's hard to know where to start because he shuns most people and is unlikely to accept help from a social worker, a nurse, or anyone who works for a statutory agency. In Unit 9, Activity 13, June Dingle talked about the difficulty of providing services for people who were 'hard to reach', and this is another term that applies to Simon.

As you have already seen, neighbourhood-based activities do not always meet the needs of everyone. Deborah Quilgars, a researcher, wrote a report evaluating the Hull Community Care Development Project. This project was set up to run for three years between 1999 and 2002, supported by a steering group which included representatives from social services, health, housing, and the voluntary and community sectors. The aim of the project was to find out whether voluntary and community organisations could meet 'the care and support needs of vulnerable people who would not qualify for statutory assistance' from the social services department (Quilgars, 2004, p. 6). Although a number of new activities were set up to meet local residents' needs, some people were left out. At the outset of the project, it was hoped that general community centre activities would cater for the social needs of people with learning difficulties, disabled people and people with mental health problems. However, Quilgars found that:

> … occasionally, community groups did not include individuals with, for example, mobility problems or mild learning difficulties [and] … the community did not feel as though it possessed the relevant skills and experience to provide … [support for] more complex social or health interventions.

(Quilgars, 2004, p. 44)

Recognising such difficulties, the Thornhill Plus You project decided to set up the Community Access Project. Community Access is a three-year project which provides a combined advocacy and outreach service for isolated and excluded people living in Thornhill. Let's suppose that George sees a poster on the noticeboard while he's working in the Natterbox Community Centre, and gets in touch with the Community Access Project. Do you think this service might help Simon? Go to the DVD and find out from the team manager, Chris Lee.

DVD

Activity 11   Community Access: an outreach and advocacy service

Allow about 30 minutes

Find Block 3, Unit 10, Activity 11 on the DVD. Listen to Chris Lee, the team manager, talking about the work of the Community Access Project. Then work your way through the activity.

Comment

The Community Access Project was set up, as Chris Lee explains, 'to work with people who are isolated and/or excluded … people who are cut off from the community or not able to get the best out of living in Thornhill'. This certainly describes Simon, but before the project can help him, an outreach worker will have to slowly and carefully build up a relationship. George might be able to act as a bridge in this respect.

The Community Access Project is funded by Thornhill Plus You. It complements the health and social care activities provided by groups such as the Thornhill Health and Wellbeing Project and Motiv8, because it reaches out to people who don't have the confidence or inclination to take part in group activities. To help people who are, as Chris Lee describes it, on the edges of the community, the work of the Community Access Project falls into two main areas: outreach and advocacy.

Chris Lee and team at the Community Access Project

3.3 Outreach

Chris explains that the first task of project workers is to actively seek out people who might need their service. This is the 'outreach' part of the project as outlined in the project's publicity below.

Outreach

We can provide practical support – helping you to travel in and access your local community.

We can be a first point of contact – acting as your link in to the community.

We are flexible and can work with you at a time and place convenient to you.

(Source: Thornhill Plus You, undated)

Outreach means service providers initiating contact with people to find out what they need. This isn't an easy task: Simon is afraid of other people, and certainly won't allow contact with anyone in authority. The outreach worker would have to go out and find Simon – perhaps near the community centre or shops, or by making the first approach through George.

Outreach is typically used to engage people from disadvantaged groups, who are unaware of services, or who may be fearful or reluctant to contact them. You might remember that in Unit 9, Activity 3, Dave Kellett suggested that to address the problem of underage drinking, workers needed to 'reach out' to young people who didn't want to attend youth clubs or community activities, and work with them in the places they actually go. In other cases, people may not have the literacy or language skills to respond to leaflets, advertisements and other written information (ODPM, 2005, p. 55). By building trust and providing support and encouragement, outreach workers help people to overcome the barriers to accessing care services.

'Gypsy Travellers ... [comprise] four separate groups. These groups are commonly known as English Gypsies, Welsh Gypsies, Scottish Gypsy Travellers and Irish Travellers. Each of these groups has a separate ethnic identity that is particularly evident from their different languages but they share many aspects of a common cultural identity as traditional Travellers or Romani people ... New Travellers, who have opted for an alternative lifestyle ... are not of the same culture' (Parry et al., 2004, p. 4).

Another group of people who may value an outreach approach are Gypsy Travellers. You will recall that in Unit 9, Dave Kellett talked about the Irish Travellers who spent half the year on the Thornhill site and the other half travelling. The Thornhill Travellers seem to be reasonably well accepted in the neighbourhood, but they don't use community services (except the schools). Instead, services such as family support and youth workers go to the caravan site.

Irish Travellers have significantly worse health than the rest of the population:

> The average life expectancy of a Traveller man is 10 years shorter than a settled man's. Traveller women live on average 12 years less than their settled peers ... Travellers have higher death rates for all causes; their rates are significantly higher for: accidents, metabolic disorders in 0–14 age group, respiratory ailments, congenital problems.
>
> (Power, 2004, p. 36)

Women in Irish Traveller communities face additional health problems:

> Stillbirth is seventeen times higher than the national average; infant mortality is twelve times higher than average rates – twice as many Traveller infants fall into the low birth weight category (Linthwaite, 1983). Traveller women's use of family planning, developmental

screening, immunisation, and antenatal care services is very low in relation to other minority groups and society in general (Pahl and Vaile, 1986).

(Power, 2004, p. 41)

In response to the health inequalities experienced by Gypsy Travellers, Friends, Families and Travellers (FFT) set up an outreach service called the Sussex Traveller Women's Health Project. Like Community Access, this project was designed to be flexible and to work with people at a time and place to suit their needs. In the next activity you will be able to find out what this involved.

Activity 12 Health outreach for Gypsy and Irish Traveller women
Allow about 15 minutes

Read the following account of the Sussex Traveller Women's Health Project, and then complete the task that follows.

Sussex Traveller Women's Health Project

This project was initially set up by FFT to address some of the health related issues experienced by the Gypsy/Traveller community in Sussex … The aim was to support Gypsy/Traveller women to become health advocates for their own families and communities …

The first six months of the project were spent visiting the authorised Gypsy sites within Sussex, getting to know the residents and identifying community leaders and advocates. This was greatly enhanced by the fact that the Outreach Worker [herself a Traveller] was already known to most of the Gypsy/Travellers through her work with the Traveller Education Service. At this stage in the project we were working closely with South Downs Adult Education who were going to supply the teaching for the project. We hosted a party and information session for all interested parties where volunteers were able to sign up for the project.

We arranged transport and childcare for all course participants who agreed to attend college for the sessions. The Outreach Worker contacted all participants the night before we were due to start the training, despite this nobody came to the first two sessions.

It was at this point that we realised it was unrealistic to expect the volunteers to come to us. It may have been different if we could have paid them adequately, but many of our volunteers were extremely busy women with many different demands upon them. In the end we took the project to our volunteers. We paid them childcare expenses, travelling expenses and a nominal amount for lunch, where this was not provided.

[…]

The first few sessions with a new group were spent getting to know each other in a relaxed and informal way. We often used craft sessions at the beginning of each new course where we would use traditional Gypsy crafts such as flower making as a way of starting our work together.

We also did a lot of cooking together and would share the food afterwards, this culminated in a collection of Traveller recipes, which we put together in

> a book. We used an artist to illustrate each recipe in a step-by-step format making it accessible to those with low levels of literacy …
>
> It was during these informal sessions that we were able to discuss health issues with the volunteers. We then supported the group to identify their own health themes and the needs from within the group.
>
> We put training sessions in place to address the themes in health that the group had identified. We also spent a lot of time supporting individuals and bridging the gaps within statutory provision.
>
> (Friends, Families and Travellers, 2005, pp. 2, 6)

Underline three points of similarity with Thornhill Plus You activities – for example, Crafty Crafters or Cooking Pots. Do you think there are any differences?

Comment

There were a number of similarities between this project and the Thornhill activities:

- The worker had the same background as the women taking part.
- One of the aims of the project was to train residents to become voluntary health workers for their own (Traveller) community.
- Similar activities were organised – craft work, cooking together and sharing meals. These were enjoyable and relaxing, and beneficial for the women's well-being.
- The residents identified the health issues that were of importance to themselves and other residents.
- The sessions took place in the women's own community (the Gypsy Traveller site).

Did you find any differences? The main difference is that the project was provided for a very specific group of people who shared the same ethnic and cultural identity. They were unlikely to come to any sessions in the local area, for the reasons outlined in Section 2.2. Another difference is that health issues were addressed indirectly at first – through the craft and cooking sessions. No particular reasons are given for this in the account, but they may be related to the Gypsy Travellers' culture and their particular approach to formal health services.

Overall, the two projects seem to be attempting to achieve similar goals, but the outreach project is taking its work out to a very marginalised group. Outreach, as you have seen from the examples of Community Access and the Traveller Women's Health Project, is a valuable approach. In its 2005 report on making services more accessible for disadvantaged adults, the Social Exclusion Unit notes that outreach services are increasing in popularity:

> Almost one in three of the service providers who responded to our consultation said that they had increased their use of community outreach over the past five years. The approach was being used to engage … disadvantaged people and the biggest increase in its use had taken place in the statutory sector.
>
> (ODPM, 2005, p. 54)

However, this growth is limited by problems to do with funding:

> Outreach is … resource intensive. And in spite of increasing use it does remain patchy – especially within the statutory sector. Outreach often depends on short-term and insecure grant funding …

> (ODPM, 2005, p. 55)

Let's return now to the Community Access Project in Thornhill. Once an outreach worker has established some kind of trust with Simon – perhaps helping him to get some treatment for his injuries – it may be possible to involve him in the project's advocacy service.

3.4 Advocacy

The word 'advocacy' can be used in different ways, but Chris Lee's explanation is that advocacy is about 'trying to help people speak up for themselves', while also 'not trying to influence in any way what they're doing'. A similar definition is used by Action for Advocacy, an organisation which supports independent advocacy schemes in England and Wales:

> Advocacy is taking action to help people say what they want, secure their rights, represent their interests and obtain services they need.

> (Action for Advocacy, undated)

Within the context of health and social care services, certain groups of people are particularly likely to benefit from advocacy to give them a voice when they are in danger of not being heard:

- adults with learning difficulties

- young people who are being looked after by the local authority

- older people with communication difficulties (such as those due to dementia)

- people with mental health problems (when they are being detained in a psychiatric hospital, for example).

Advocacy has a long history, but in the last twenty years it has moved from being 'on the fringe of things' to 'centre stage' (Forbat and Atkinson, 2005, p. 325). Liz Forbat and Dorothy Atkinson argue that the recent growth in advocacy schemes has been boosted by government policies that promote social inclusion:

> *Valuing People* (Department of Health, 2001a) … clearly articulates the importance of advocacy in relation to people with learning difficulties … Advocacy has also gained recognition in policy documents relating to older people, e.g. in *The National Service Framework for Older People* (Department of Health, 2001b). Similarly … the *National Strategy for Carers* (Department of Health, 1999) points to a role for advocates in enabling carers to access benefits and services.

> (Forbat and Atkinson, 2005, pp. 325–6)

Some people with mental health problems are legally entitled to advocacy, although this depends on which part of the UK they live in. In Scotland, for example, the Mental Health (Care and Treatment) (Scotland) Act 2003 gives all people who use mental health services the right to access an independent advocate who can support them to express their views about their care and treatment (Scottish Government, 2004).

Advocacy is about helping people to say what they want, and to secure their rights

Independent advocacy

Advocacy is a way of helping people on the edges of a community – powerless and excluded people – to have a voice. Independent advocacy services often operate according to a set of nationally agreed principles called the Advocacy Charter. This emphasises that advocates should be independent from service providers. It also states that advocates should be non-judgemental, helping the person to present their own views, regardless of whether they agree or disagree with them. In the box below, you will see that these principles are incorporated into the Thornhill Community Access Project's statement of what it offers.

Advocacy

- We will help you to get your views and opinions heard and listened to.
- We will work with you to make sure you are involved in decision-making.
- We will listen and provide a voice.
- We will guard your rights and freedom of choice.
- We can challenge services – making sure there are real improvements for you.
- We will not counsel or give advice.
- We will not make decisions on your behalf or decide what is in your best interest.

(Source: Thornhill Plus You, undated)

Do you think independent advocacy will be of benefit to Simon?

Activity 13   The benefits of independent advocacy

Allow about 15 minutes

Look at the principles that underpin advocacy, summarised in the box above.
Then complete the grid below with some examples of how these principles could
be applied in Simon's case. The final row of the grid invites you to jot down your
ideas about how advocacy can support Simon to live in the community.

Community Access Project principles	Example of how these principles would apply in Simon's case
'We will help you to get your views and opinions heard and listened to'	Perhaps Simon wants to express his feelings about being banned from the community centre? An advocate could go with him to talk with the community workers
'We will work with you to make sure you are involved in decision-making'	
'We will listen and provide a voice'	
'We will guard your rights and freedom of choice'	
'We can challenge services – making sure there are real improvements for you'	
'We will not counsel or give advice'	
'We will not make decisions on your behalf or decide what is in your best interest'	
How can advocacy support Simon to live in the community?	

Comment

Compare your responses with those given below.

Community Access Project principles	Example of how these principles would apply in Simon's case
'We will help you to get your views and opinions heard and listened to'	Perhaps Simon wants to express his feelings about being banned from the community centre? An advocate could go with him to talk with the community workers
'We will work with you to make sure you are involved in decision-making'	If decisions need to be made about Simon's health care (a referral to mental health services, for example), an advocate would help him to have a say in his treatment
'We will listen and provide a voice'	What does Simon feel about his situation? An advocate would spend time simply listening to Simon and helping him to put his thoughts and concerns into words. He is so isolated that he doesn't usually have the opportunity to talk to anyone
'We will guard your rights and freedom of choice'	Does Simon want to press charges against the people who beat him up? The advocate can help him to understand his legal rights and the implications of reporting the incident. If Simon decides not to do this, the advocate will respect his wishes
'We can challenge services – making sure there are real improvements for you'	Supposing Simon wants his front door lock mended. Has he already asked housing to do this, and if so, why is it still broken? An advocate could – with Simon's approval – put some pressure on services to get things put right
'We will not counsel or give advice'	The advocate might consider that Simon drinks too much alcohol. The advocate wouldn't try to offer any health advice, but through listening carefully to Simon, would find out if this is of concern to him. If it is, then the advocate would help Simon to get advice on reducing his intake
'We will not make decisions on your behalf or decide what is in your best interest'	The advocate wouldn't take any actions without Simon's involvement. For example, the advocate wouldn't do anything about arranging for electricity to be restored and the graffiti on Simon's door to be removed unless he wanted this
How can advocacy support Simon to live in the community?	Having an advocate would help Simon to engage with people and services in his neighbourhood, on terms that are acceptable to him. This would help him to improve his well-being. An advocate would also make Simon aware of his rights – for example, making sure he knew about social security benefits and legal protection

As you can see, an independent advocate would help Simon to make changes for the better in his life, at his own pace and without feeling judged. He might choose to remain 'on the margins' of the community, but at least he would have support to use services if he wishes.

Advocacy and care work

You might have noted from the Tower Hamlets Family Support Service and the Age Concern project that advocacy is sometimes considered part of a care worker's role. In the Age Concern scheme (Resource 8), 'service users needed social care project workers to act as advocates in negotiations with key organizations and networks, to obtain material and social resources'. In Mina's case:

> ... mental health problems were the initial assessment by the referrer but ... [the worker] was able to clarify the context, personal circumstances and difficulties of the individual involved ... [thus illustrating] the importance of the FSS's advocacy ... getting a balance by listening to the point of view of families ...

> (Gray, 2003, p. 372)

Listening to people and finding out about their needs is an important aspect of health and social care work. People may also need care workers' help to gain access to other services, and in some cases to help them to express their views. Nurses see advocacy as a central part of their role, and in some cases regard it as an obligation (Hewitt, 2002). The most recent version of the Nursing and Midwifery Council's code of conduct tells nurses:

> You must act as an advocate for those in your care, helping them to access relevant health and social care, information and support

> (Nursing and Midwifery Council, 2007)

How does this view of advocacy sit with the idea that advocates should be independent from service providers? Jeannette Hewitt (2002, p. 442), writing from a nurse's perspective, suggests that advocacy carried out as part of a professional relationship is 'difficult to separate ... from simple "caring" and the use of effective interpersonal skills'. For example, a hospital patient might want a nurse to ask the doctor a question on their behalf. Or the patient might ask the nurse or health care worker to restrict visitors if they are tired but don't want to offend people. This form of advocacy goes on all the time, and doesn't require the nurse or care worker to be 'independent' because all they are doing is expressing the patient's wishes. In these situations, it is still possible to be a good advocate even though one may not be independent.

However, when the patient's wishes involve challenging hospital policy or a colleague's professional judgement, this is a different matter. In these situations it can be difficult for nurses to act as independent advocates. Reviewing the nursing literature, Hewitt puts forward a number of obstacles which could arise for nurses who wish to act as independent advocates:

> Doctors have felt threatened by nurse advocacy and its encroachment on their traditional role as information givers (Marshall 1991). As a result of this hostility, nurses have been fearful to speak out for patients, even when patients were suffering, due to the effects this might have on their careers (Beardshaw 1981).
>
> [...]
>
> ... Conflicting demands from different patients may create ethical conflicts (Woodrow 1997) ...
>
> ... Nurses may be restricted from independent action as an advocate, due to accountability to their employers.

> (Hewitt, 2002, pp. 441–2)

To prevent conflicts of interest, advocacy is usually provided by specialist organisations in the voluntary sector. Community Access, for example, although funded by Thornhill Plus You, is managed by an independent organisation called Choices Advocacy (www.choices-advocacy.org.uk). Community Access works with all groups of people, but some advocacy organisations are geared to specific services. For example, a London hospital offers a bilingual health advocacy service for people who do not speak English and need support when dealing with health staff. Have a look at the extract from their website, given in the box below.

Health advocacy

Staff at the hospital work hard to understand the needs of the patients and visitors who come here. We know that coming to hospital can sometimes be a frightening and frustrating time for those patients who do not speak English as their first language.

[…]

What is bilingual health advocacy?

Bilingual interpretation for:

- patients who do not speak or read fluent English
- advice, information and support to help people access health services
- educating health services about cultural norms so they can provide care and treatment in a culturally sensitive way.

(Source: Homerton University Hospital, undated)

In their evaluation of advocacy schemes in Nottingham, Forbat and Atkinson (2005) conclude that advocacy is effective and 'makes a difference'. In similar vein, the Social Exclusion Unit has acknowledged that independent advocacy helps disadvantaged adults to get better access to health and social care services. The SEU's 2005 report recognised the important advocacy role played by voluntary and community organisations, but found that they are frequently hampered by short-term or inadequate funding (ODPM, 2005, p. 55). Insecure funding results in a patchy service, and consequently, advocacy 'is not there for everyone who needs it' (Forbat and Atkinson, 2005, p. 328). For example, nurses frequently have to provide care for people who are unconscious, and:

> As yet there would seem to be little evidence of independent advocates working … with the 'silent patients' of the intensive care unit and other individuals unable to give or refuse consent.

(Hewitt, 2002, p. 443)

So while independent advocacy is the ideal, appropriate services may not be available everywhere. Advocacy that is carried out during the course of a care worker's day-to-day job is different from the model of independent advocacy promoted by the Advocacy Charter. However, some health and social care workers take the view that if they don't advocate on behalf of service users, no one else will. The Nursing and Midwifery Council has issued advice for nurses who find themselves in an advocacy role: the 'A–Z advice sheet'. You can find this, if you wish to look at it, in the Resources Book (Resource 11). You will also find there a copy of Action for Advocacy's 'The Advocacy Charter: defining and promoting key advocacy' (Resource 12).

Resources

Through the case study of Simon, you have thought about the more negative aspects of communities and the effects of social exclusion on health and well-being. You have also looked at two initiatives which are rapidly gaining popularity in community health and social care provision: outreach and advocacy. The final section of this unit invites you to revisit what you have learned in Units 9 and 10, and review the successes of neighbourhood renewal projects.

Key points

- Communities are not inclusive for everyone; some people are excluded and 'on the margins'.

- Outreach is a way of helping disadvantaged people to overcome the barriers they face in taking up services.

- Advocacy means helping people to say what they want, represent their interests, safeguard their rights, and obtain services they need.

- To avoid conflicts of interest, independent advocacy services are usually provided by the voluntary and community sector.

- Both outreach and advocacy services rely on short-term and insecure grant funding, and consequently are not available to everyone who needs them.

4 Reviewing 'community' and neighbourhood renewal

There are different ways of thinking about communities. They are all characterised by a sense of belonging: to the places where people live; to networks of social relationships; and on the basis of shared identity. Each kind of community offers possibilities for providing support with health and social care needs. In this final section, you look back at the neighbourhood activities and other services you have read and heard about in Block 3 so far. How do they relate to the different meanings of community? And how successful are they in improving people's well-being?

4.1 A recap on neighbourhood renewal and communities

In Unit 9 you read about the work of Thornhill Plus You, an example of a neighbourhood renewal project. This section begins by revisiting the aims and principles that characterise neighbourhood renewal.

Neighbourhood renewal

Thornhill Plus You – one of thirty-nine programmes funded under the New Deal for Communities (NDC) initiative – is part of the government's broad strategy for neighbourhood renewal. The aim of neighbourhood renewal is to reduce the problems of social exclusion and improve people's quality of life in severely deprived areas. Although Units 9 and 10 have focused on health and well-being, neighbourhood renewal takes a much wider approach, which also addresses issues to do with educational achievement, employment, housing and crime.

Neighbourhood renewal draws on extensive research evidence which indicates that health and other inequalities are associated with where people live, interlinked with factors such as income, social class and ethnicity. The government's response has been to target resources at disadvantaged neighbourhoods. Thornhill was eligible to apply for NDC funding only because it was defined as an area with a high level of deprivation.

Thornhill residents worked with local professionals to set health targets based on the neighbourhood's particular needs. The most recent survey found that there had been significant improvements, including:

- more people eating healthily
- fewer people smoking
- more people taking part in physical exercise
- more people with better health than a year previously
- better access to health services.

(Adapted from Thornhill Plus You, 2006)

It is clear that the services and activities you read about or saw in Unit 9 are improving health for the people who use them. This unit has explored the needs of people who, for a variety of reasons, are unable or reluctant to use ordinary community services. However, targeted approaches, such as Thornhill Family Support, and outreach projects, such as Community Access, can form a bridge in order to help socially excluded people to benefit from what communities can offer.

Communities and support

At the beginning of this unit you considered the different meanings of community associated with place, social networks and shared identity. In the next activity, you explore the links between these meanings and the activities and services you have learned about so far in Block 3.

Activity 14   Different communities and their potential for support

Allow about 15 minutes

Think about the three meanings of community and the kind of support they can offer. For each one:

(a) Jot down some ideas about the kind of support that it offers.

(b) Find an example of how this support is provided by one of the services you have read about in Block 3 (not necessarily from Thornhill).

Use the grid below for your answers. The first row has been filled in to help you, but you can add to this if you wish.

Meanings of community	How does this provide support?	Example from Block 3
Place	Support is organised around a neighbourhood or other locality	Breastfeeding support group at the Thornhill Centre for Healthy Living
Social networks		
Identity		

Comment

As you read on, compare your responses with the ideas below.

Care services are usually organised around a particular locality or neighbourhood. This can have disadvantages; for example, people who move around a lot (such as Travellers and people seeking asylum) and are without a fixed address may find it difficult to access health and social care services. However, locality-based support has worked well in neighbourhood renewal areas such as Thornhill, where residents have been able to influence the design of services. Examples of this kind of support in Thornhill include the Centre for Healthy Living, the Thornhill Health and Wellbeing Project and Motiv8.

Support can also come from people's social networks. In this unit, you have seen examples of services designed to help excluded people develop supportive networks: the Age Concern project, Thornhill Family Support, the Tower Hamlets Family Support Service, and the Community Access Project.

Finally, support can be organised around communities of identity. An example is outreach work with Travellers. The Thornhill Travellers didn't take part in the DVD, and so they haven't featured in Units 9 and 10. Instead, you heard about the Sussex Traveller Women's Health Project, which provided health information to women who shared a cultural identity. The project worked with the women at a time and place which met their particular cultural needs. In Unit 11, you will explore further the idea of culturally sensitive services.

Although government policies tend to emphasise the idea of community as a place, Thornhill Plus You – and other community initiatives – are recognising that developing services around place alone is not sufficient. There is an awareness of the need to use targeted approaches to include people who are on the margins of a neighbourhood.

4.2 Making the changes last

Reflecting on the progress of Thornhill Plus You, its Director Dave Kellett says that:

> One of the difficulties for physical regeneration is actually it takes a long time … because of planning and because of the way that one needs to involve people.

(Dave Kellett, interview, 22 March 2007)

And yet the programme receives funding only for ten years. Critics of neighbourhood renewal policies regard this as one of its limitations. Certainly the constraint on funding makes it hard to know whether NDC programmes will have lasting effects. Paul Brigden (2004, p. 292), for example, reviewing the successes and challenges of community health projects, observes that 'any changes to the external environment as a result of a community-based scheme are only likely to occur in the longer term'. The NDC initiative was set up to find out what would work in the longer term, not just in specific neighbourhoods, but everywhere. This seems like a good idea, but where does it leave people who actually live in Thornhill? Will the efforts of volunteers and paid workers evaporate once the programme is disbanded? Before ending your work for this unit, return to the DVD to find out how Thornhill Plus You plans to continue and finance its work once the NDC funding comes to an end.

DVD

Activity 15   Planning for the future

Allow about 20 minutes

What will happen to Thornhill Plus You when the funding runs out? Will all the activities and services grind to a halt? Here you find out from the programme's staff and volunteers.

Find Block 3, Unit 10, Activity 15 on the DVD.

Comment

As you heard from the audio, plans have been made for ensuring that the activities of Thornhill Plus You will be able to continue after the NDC funding has ended. New sources of funding have been identified, and some responsibilities will be handed over to statutory agencies such as Southampton City Council and the primary care trust. Local volunteers will continue to play an even bigger role in the neighbourhood, ideally with their own grant-aided funding.

New Deal for Communities projects can have a long-term impact only when they are designed to last. As Ruth Chiddle put it:

> … you have to think from the start, how you are going to 'succeed' the project, and how you are going to mainstream it … Because otherwise it's just money that's down the drain. It … comes to an abrupt end, and then you're … left with a terrible vacuum. And that … makes the area poorer than when it started, because … the things that were being done on a voluntary basis before, they're no longer there either, and then things are much poorer.

(DVD, Block 3, Unit 10, Activity 15 audio)

Although many of Thornhill's community projects will become the responsibility of mainstream agencies, there will continue to be a significant reliance on voluntary organisations. In preparation for this, the volunteers who support the Thornhill Health and Wellbeing Project are doing a considerable amount of training, and are beginning to run activities alongside the paid workers. The plans for carrying on the work of Thornhill Plus You will increase the demands on local people's involvement. Will this be successful? Time will tell: but residents are committed to the neighbourhood, and determined to change it for the better. In addition, they now have a wealth of community work experience to draw on.

In Chapter 10 in the Reader, which you read for Unit 9, Lynsey Hanley argued that social housing tenants need to feel 'a sense of ownership and control … as if the estate is theirs' (p. 88). Residents' involvement has been a requirement of NDC programmes, and it is not clear how far they will be able to influence health and social care developments once the funding ends. However, as Dave Kellett mentioned, the Thornhill Plus You programme is taking steps to set up a system of 'neighbourhood management':

> This will enable local people to have a voice in how services are delivered by agencies such as the City Council [and] the Primary Care Trust …

(Thornhill Plus You, 2007, p. 22)

A resident shows off the costume she has made for the Thornhill Carnival. Community events like these, supported by Thornhill Plus You, have enabled people to develop a sense of pride in their neighbourhood.

Thornhill Plus You has achieved a lot since its beginnings. Along with the physical and environmental improvements, there have been improvements in local health and in access to services. The participation of local residents has been central to the success of the programme. The last word, however, goes to Dave Shields, Manager of the Thornhill Health and Wellbeing Project:

> I think this is wonderful what we've managed to achieve in Thornhill, but I want to be able to do this in all the other places that are like Thornhill in the area … I am sure the people in Thornhill would agree … it's worked for them, and other communities deserve exactly the same.

(Dave Shields, interview 22 March 2007)

Key points

- Evaluations show that neighbourhood renewal is improving people's health and well-being.
- Although policies usually focus on localities, it is important to recognise the support that can be offered by other forms of community based on social networks and shared identity.
- Neighbourhood renewal is most likely to be effective when its activities are designed to be sustained beyond the life of short-term projects.

Conclusion

You began this unit by considering the different meanings of community associated with place, social networks and shared identity. Each of these offers different ways of supporting people, sometimes based around a neighbourhood and at other times across a distance. Social networks can be a significant source of support, and have benefits for people's health and well-being. However, vulnerable or disadvantaged people may lack the means to develop supportive networks.

You have seen a variety of ways in which care services can help people to strengthen their connections with others in the community. Universal services – designed for open access by everybody – are valuable, but may not be enough for people who have complex needs or who are excluded. Targeted services – available only to people who meet specific criteria – are an important addition to community-based activities. Ideally, both kinds of service need to be provided together, to help people to remain connected with ordinary social networks in their neighbourhood. You have also looked at two approaches – outreach and advocacy – which can help powerless and excluded people to obtain support and have a voice.

Finally, you have reviewed the success of neighbourhood renewal projects. You saw that to sustain benefits over the long term, careful planning is needed to ensure that they can continue beyond the life of short-term funding.

Although government policies tend to emphasise the idea of community as a place, it is important to recognise that within localities there may be other forms of community which cut across geographical boundaries, or operate in tandem with them. In this unit you have briefly considered communities of identity, and these may be especially significant for some groups of people whose perspectives are excluded or hidden in neighbourhoods. Unit 11 will take up this theme in relation to diversity and discrimination in health and social care.

Learning skills: How much are you remembering?

You have completed your tenth unit of K101, but do you worry that you are forgetting everything as quickly as you read it? If you do, you can be sure you are not alone. New ideas and information are always quite loosely formed in your head and hard to get hold of. Also, reading about new ideas messes up the organisation of your mind, so that you find it harder to find your way to what you are searching for. So don't be alarmed if you seem to be forgetting a lot of what you read. A course like this isn't primarily about 'remembering', it's about 'understanding'. If you are managing to make some sense of what you read, then the right things are happening in your mind. As you work your way through the course, the ideas in it gradually grow more familiar and they become part of the way you think. Then they will be 'in' your mind and you won't have to worry about remembering them.

On the other hand, there are things you can do to make new ideas and information more memorable. You can read about some of these in Section 6.3 of *The Good Study Guide* (pages 142–8).

Reader

Learning skills: Tackling the assignment

Now that you are halfway through Block 3, how are you shaping up to your next assignment? With two blocks' worth of experience behind you, what have you learned about the writing process? In fact, how has the essay writing gone generally? Have you found it a struggle to get your ideas together and get the writing done? Did writing the essay turn your week upside down? Were you a pain to family and friends?

Did reading the first two sections of Chapter 11 of *The Good Study Guide* help? (You read these in conjunction with Unit 8.) Did you find you could break the essay work into stages, as suggested in the table on page 315, and work on them a bit at a time? How will you organise your work for TMA 04? Why not try jotting down a plan of attack now, and then see whether you can stick to it.

End-of-unit checklist

Studying this unit should have helped you to:

- outline some different meanings of 'community', in relation to people's health and well-being
- explain what is meant by 'social networks' and why these are relevant for health and social care workers to know about
- discuss what local care services can do to respond to the needs of people who are isolated and 'hard to reach'
- understand the benefits of advocacy and outreach services for excluded groups of people
- consider how time-limited neighbourhood renewal programmes can be effective in the longer term.

References

Action for Advocacy (undated) *About Advocacy* [online], www.actionforadvocacy.org.uk/ (Accessed 7 March 2008).

Beardshaw, V. (1981) *Conscientious Objectors at Work*, London, Social Audit.

Brigden, P. (2004) 'Evaluating the empowering potential of community-based health schemes: the case of community health policies in the UK since 1997', *Community Development Journal*, vol. 39, no. 3, pp. 288–301.

Buchanan, A. (2007) 'Including the socially excluded: the impact of government policy on vulnerable families and children in need', *British Journal of Social Work*, vol. 37, no. 2, pp. 187–207.

Department of Health (DH) (1999) *National Strategy for Carers*, London, The Stationery Office.

Department of Health (DH) (2001a) *Valuing People: A New Strategy for Learning Disability for the 21st Century*, London, The Stationery Office.

Department of Health (DH) (2001b) *National Service Framework for Older People*, London, The Stationery Office.

Department of Health (DH) (2005) *Independence, Well-being and Choice: Our Vision for the Future of Social Care for Adults in England* [online], www.dh.gov.uk/en/ Publicationsandstatistics/Publications/PublicationsPolicyAndGuidance/DH_4106477 (Accessed 7 March 2008).

East London and City Health Authority (ELCHA) (1995) *Health in the East End*, London, Department of Public Health Medicine/ELCHA.

Edwards, L. (2004) *The Lever Fabergé Family Report 2004: Parenting Under the Microscope*, London, IPPR [online], www.ippr.org.uk/publicationsandreports/? title=&author=&policyarea=0&pubdate=&pg=21 (Accessed 7 March 2008).

Every Child Matters, Change for Children (2006) *Glossary: Targeted Services* [online], www.everychildmatters.gov.uk/deliveringservices/multiagencyworking/glossary/ ?asset=glossary&id=22534 (Accessed 7 March 2008).

Forbat, L. and Atkinson, D. (2005) 'Advocacy in practice: the troubled position of advocates in adult services', *British Journal of Social Work*, vol. 35, no. 3, pp. 321–35.

Friends, Families and Travellers (2005) *Sussex Traveller Women's Health Project: Final Report 2003–2006* [online], www.gypsy-traveller.org/pdfs/health_annual_ report_05.pdf (Accessed 7 March 2008).

Ghate, D. and Hazel, N. (2002) *Parenting in Poor Environments: Stress, Support and Coping*, London, Jessica Kingsley.

Gray, B. (2003) 'Social exclusion, poverty, health and social care in Tower Hamlets: the perspectives of families on the impact of the Family Support Service', *British Journal of Social Work*, vol. 33, no. 3, pp. 361–80.

Harris, K. and Gale, T. (2004) *Looking Out for Each Other: The Manchester Neighbourliness Review*, Community Development Foundation [online], www.cdf.org.uk (Accessed 7 March 2008).

Hewitt, J. (2002) 'A critical review of the arguments debating the role of the nurse advocate', *Journal of Advanced Nursing*, vol. 37, no. 5, pp. 439–45.

Homerton University Hospital (undated) *Health Advocacy*, Homerton University Hospital NHS Foundation Trust [online], www.homerton.nhs.uk/patients/languages.html (Accessed 7 March 2008).

Linthwaite, P. (1983) *Health and Health Care in Traveller Mothers and Children*, London, Save the Children Fund.

Marshall, M. (1991) 'Advocacy within the multidisciplinary team', *Nursing Standard*, vol. 6, pp. 28–31.

Nazroo, J. (1997) *The Health of Britain's Ethnic Minorities*, London, Policy Studies Institute.

Nursing and Midwifery Council (2007) *The Code: Standards of Conduct, Performance and Ethics for Nurses and Midwives* [online], www.nmc-uk.org/aFrameDisplay. aspx?DocumentID=3954 (Accessed 21 June 2008).

Office of the Deputy Prime Minister (ODPM) (2005) *Improving Services, Improving Lives: Evidence and Key Themes: A Social Exclusion Unit Interim Report*, London, Office of the Deputy Prime Minister; also available online at http://archive. cabinetoffice.gov.uk/seu/publicationsa733.html (Accessed 7 March 2008).

Pahl, J. and Vaile, M. (1986) *Health and Health Care Among Travellers*, University of Kent, Health Research Unit.

Parry, G., Van Cleemput, P., Peters, J., Moore, J., Walters, S., Thomas, K. and Cooper, C. (2004) *The Health Status of Gypsies & Travellers in England: Summary of a Report to the Department of Health*, Sheffield, University of Sheffield, School of Health and Related Research [online], www.shef.ac.uk/scharr/research/publications/travellers.html (Accessed 7 March 2008).

Phillipson, C., Bernard, M., Phillips, J. and Ogg, J. (2001) *The Family and Community Life of Older People: Social Networks and Social Support in Three Urban Areas*, London, Routledge.

Power, C. (2004) *Room to Roam: England's Irish Travellers* [online], www.irishtraveller.org.uk/policy/room-to-roam (Accessed 7 March 2008).

Putnam, R.D. (2000) *Bowling Alone: The Collapse and Revival of American Community*, New York, Simon & Schuster.

Quilgars, D. (2004) *Communities Caring and Developing: Lessons from Hull*, York, Joseph Rowntree Foundation; also available online at www.jrf.org.uk/bookshop/ eBooks/1859351905.pdf (Accessed 7 March 2008).

Roberts, E. (1984) *A Woman's Place: An Oral History of Working Class Women 1890–1940*, Oxford, Blackwell.

Scottish Government (2004) *The New Mental Health Act – What's It All About?: A Short Introduction* [online], www.scotland.gov.uk/Publications/2004/01/18753/31686 (Accessed 15 May 2008).

Stacey, M. (1969) 'The myth of community studies', *British Journal of Sociology*, vol. 20, no. 2, pp. 134–47.

Thornhill Plus You (2006) *People and Progress, Delivery Plan 2006–2011* [online], www.thornhillplusyou.co.uk/documents/HI_DP_Apendicies.pdf (Accessed 7 March 2008).

Thornhill Plus You (2007) *Growing the Future, Delivery Plan 2007–2011* [online], www.thornhillplusyou.co.uk/deliveryplan2007.asp (Accessed 18 November 2007).

Thornhill Plus You (undated) *Thornhill Community Access Project* [online], www. thornhillplusyou.co.uk/myhealth/communityaccess.asp (Accessed 7 March 2008).

Tower Hamlets Council (undated) *Borough Statistics* [online], www.towerhamlets.gov. uk/data/discover/data/borough-profile/index.cfm (Accessed 7 March 2008).

Van Cleemput, P., Thomas, K., Parry, G., Peters, J., Moore, J. and Cooper, C. (2004) *The Health Status of Gypsies and Travellers in England: Report of Qualitative Findings*, University of Sheffield, School of Health and Related Research [online], www.shef.ac.uk/scharr/research/publications/travellers.html (Accessed 7 March 2008).

Waddell, H. (2006) 'Who will believe him?', *Community Care*, 5 January [online], www.communitycare.co.uk/Articles/2006/01/05/52287/who-will-believe-him.html (Accessed 7 March 2008).

Willmott, P. with Thomas, D. (1984) *Community in Social Policy*, London, Policy Studies Institute.

Woodrow, P. (1997) 'Nurse advocacy: is it in the patient's best interests?', *British Journal of Nursing*, vol. 6, pp. 225–9.

Young, M. and Willmott, P. (1957) *Family and Kinship in East London*, London, Routledge and Kegan Paul.

Website

www.choices-advocacy.org.uk (Accessed 7 March 2008).

Unit 11

Working with diversity

Prepared for the course team by Fran Wiles

Contents

Introduction

As you have seen in Units 9 and 10, government policy focuses on 'the community' as both a source of support and a place where care takes place. However, communities are made up of people who have very different backgrounds, experiences and beliefs. Living in the same place does not necessarily create a sense of belonging. Some people feel more attached to a community based on shared identity than to one based on geographical closeness.

Unit 11 explores how difference affects both the delivery of care and the experience of receiving it. The main focus will be on people from minority ethnic groups, disabled people and older lesbians and gay men. However, as you work through the unit you will find examples of other kinds of difference too.

The unit starts by exploring the concepts of diversity and communities of identity. In Section 2 you will begin to look at how the processes of stereotyping, prejudice and discrimination have a detrimental effect on the quality of health and social care provision. This leads, in Section 3, to a consideration of what it is like to experience discrimination, drawing on case studies about racism against care workers and service users. Finally, in Section 4 you will read and hear about positive approaches with which employers and workers can respond to diversity, and challenge prejudice and discrimination.

You may find that the material in this unit evokes personal memories and experiences of exclusion or discrimination. Your own experience can be used in a positive way, to help you think about the perspectives of the people discussed in this unit. However, if you find this distressing, it may be helpful to talk about your feelings with a family member or friend.

Core questions

- What is social diversity, and why is it a challenge to the delivery of care services?
- What is meant by stereotyping, prejudice and discrimination, and how do they affect the quality of care for service users?
- What is racism, and why is it difficult for care workers to talk about it?
- How can organisations respond positively to diversity and provide inclusive workplaces and services?

Are you taking the IVR?

If you are studying K101 as part of the Integrated Vocational Route (IVR), don't forget to check your VQ Candidate Handbook to see which Unit 11 activities contribute to your electronic portfolio.

1 Diversity in communities

This section explores the concept of diversity, and draws on the idea that people belong to 'communities of identity' based on shared experience. Communities of identity can be a source of strength, but this strength may have developed from shared adversity.

1.1 Diversity

Health and social care agencies often claim – for example, in their publicity and recruitment advertising – that they value diversity. What does that mean? Here's what a housing organisation says on its website:

> **What we mean by valuing diversity**
>
> Bolton is a diverse community in terms of factors such as culture, ethnicity, age, disability, income and health. Bolton at Home values this diversity.
>
> [...]
>
> *We want our services, facilities and resources to be accessible and useful to everyone, regardless of race, ethnic origin, disability, nationality, gender, sexual orientation, age, class, appearance, religion, responsibility for dependants, unrelated criminal activities,*[*] *being HIV positive or having AIDS, or any other characteristic which may unfairly affect a person's opportunities in life. We will take positive action to promote equality and fair treatment and ensure that individual needs are met.*
>
> (Bolton at Home, undated)

[*This means a minor conviction that has no impact on the individual's ability or suitability to carry out the job.]

In this statement the organisation is signalling, first, its recognition that the local community contains a wide mix of people, and second, its commitment to making its services appropriate for everyone. But how and why should it do this?

Activity 1   What does diversity mean?

Allow about 10 minutes

Looking at the statement again, jot down your ideas in response to the following questions:

(a) Is diversity being presented as a positive or a negative thing?

(b) The examples refer to a range of personal characteristics (such as age and ethnicity). Are these all of a similar kind? If not, how are they different from each other?

(c) Take just one characteristic and make a note of how it might affect someone's opportunities in life.

(d) Can you think of any examples from earlier in the course where people have received 'less equal' treatment on the basis of their difference from others?

Comment

Compare your answers with the following:

(a) The statement presents diversity as something to be valued, but at the same time it suggests that the characteristics that make people different from each other can also be the basis for inequality.

(b) Some of the characteristics are ones that people are born with, while others are ones they may come to acquire during the course of their life. Some differences are easily visible; others are less obvious. People who tested K101 also pointed out that some kinds of diversity affect people more negatively than others. One said that: 'not all kinds of diversity lead to inequality – for example being a UK citizen with French parents doesn't affect your access to health or social care'.

(c) As you saw from the Acheson Report in Unit 9, people's health can be influenced by such things as their age, their social class and whether they have a disability. Taking one person's situation as an example, Thornhill resident David Buckman told how his long-term health condition had caused him to become unemployed and lose his accommodation.

(d) There are many examples from earlier units. You might have mentioned James Lappin (Unit 7) being deprived of a family life as a young child and spending most of his subsequent years at Lennox Castle Hospital, because he was labelled 'mentally handicapped' at a time when that often led to segregation. Simon (Unit 10), who had mental health problems, experienced hostility in the neighbourhood, and this made it difficult for him to take advantage of community-based services. Mina (also Unit 10) was diagnosed incorrectly (and thus denied appropriate treatment) because her different culture and language impeded communication with health professionals.

Valuing diversity, therefore, involves recognising both that people are different, and that this difference can be the basis for inequality.

Celebrating Chinese
New Year in a UK city

1.2 Valuing difference

The 'Bolton at Home' statement reflects a way of thinking that is known as the 'diversity approach'. This approach is often adopted by health and social care services. Neil Thompson explains that it is characterised by two key ideas:

1. … diversity (that is, variety and difference) is … seen as an asset, a positive feature of society that enriches our experience – it is something that should be valued, affirmed and even celebrated …

2. … any form of unfair discrimination is a problem to be tackled … regardless of whether the discrimination in question is illegal or not.

(Thompson, 2006, p. 11)

Valuing diversity means that care services take account of the differences in people's lifestyles and family relationships, determined by such factors as culture and social class. In Unit 2 you were introduced to the concept of culturally sensitive services. You will remember that this was of particular importance for Anwar Malik, because initially he was given diabetic dietary advice that took no account of the way he and his family cooked and ate at home. It was only when a specialist nurse provided a diet sheet suited to his cultural needs that Anwar Malik was able to start controlling his diabetes. To get a feel for what else might be involved in culturally sensitive care, in the next activity you will consider a very different kind of service: short breaks for black and minority ethnic disabled children. Short breaks (sometimes known as respite care) can be:

> … anything from a few hours a week to a few days a month. They may take place in the child's own home, the home of an approved carer or family or in a community setting. Short breaks can include day, evening, weekend or overnight care, Saturday and after-school clubs, befriending and inclusive leisure activities.

(Resource 13, p. 65)

What does 'black and minority ethnic' mean?

In this unit you will come across the term 'black and minority ethnic', used to describe some people's ethnic group. Elsewhere, you may see this shortened to 'BME'. The Scottish Government website explains that:

> The term 'black/minority ethnic' refers to communities whose origins lie mainly in South Asia (e.g. India, Pakistan, Bangladesh, Sri Lanka), Africa, The Caribbean (originally Africa), and China. It can be used to mean groups who would not define themselves as 'white' (the term 'black' may also be used in this case).

(Scottish Government, 2003)

The term 'black' is sometimes also used to convey a shared experience of migration and discrimination (Butt, 2006).

Everyone has an ethnic group. 'The term "minority ethnic" refers to groups who are in the minority', defined in relation to the 'majority ethnic' group (although this term is not often used). So, for example, in the UK as a whole, 'minority ethnic' groups include refugees and asylum seekers, Gypsy Travellers, Polish and Italian communities, as well as groups covered under the term 'black and minority ethnic'. In Scotland, it also includes English and Irish people (Scottish Government, 2003).

Research has shown that disabled children – like other children – value the opportunity to experience new activities and relationships away from home (Tarleton and Macaulay, 2002). And as you might recall from the story of Ann and Angus, respite care is also an essential ingredient which enables family carers to continue caring and to prevent family breakdown. However, black and Asian families do not use short break care as often as white families do. Ronny Flynn (2002) found that this is not because black and Asian families don't need services (contrary to the popular misconception that 'they look after their own'), but because they don't know about them, and when they do seek services they find that they are not culturally sensitive.

Disabled children and their families value having respite carers who can provide a familiar cultural environment

Resources

Activity 2 Culturally sensitive care for disabled children

Allow about 20 minutes

Turn to Resource 13, 'Improving access to services for black and minority ethnic disabled children', by Shameem Nawaz. You will be using this article again in Section 4, but for now just read the two sections headed 'Matching and linking' and 'Transracial placements'. Find a few examples of why it's important for black and minority ethnic disabled children to be matched with carers from the same ethnic community.

Comment

You might have selected some of the following reasons:

- It's important for disabled children to be cared for in a familiar environment which is similar to home – this is especially true for children with sensory impairments who rely on their senses of smell, sight, touch and sound.

- There may be particular dietary requirements; for example, for Halal meat.

- If the children have a particular religion this will be respected.

- Carers can communicate in the child's language.

- Carers can provide strong black role models to help black and minority ethnic children develop a positive sense of who they are and deal with racism.
- Children may have particular routines regarding hair and skin care.

Resource 13 highlights that recognising and meeting people's cultural requirements is important. It also makes the point that culturally sensitive care is not just based on skin colour, and in certain situations can be provided by people whose ethnic background is different from that of the service user.

Care services have to be fair to everyone. One approach is to treat everyone the same. But this doesn't always work, as you saw in the case of Anwar Malik's diabetic diet sheet. Another interesting example comes from the field of community-based palliative care, where specialist nurses provide 'symptom management' – and especially pain control – for terminally ill people in their own homes. Owens and Randhawa (2004) found that white nurses felt uneasy about taking the same approach to South Asian patients as they did to white patients. The underlying philosophy of the palliative care service was founded on 'listening to the patient's needs and then being guided by their wishes' which required a certain amount of 'standing back' and letting patients take the lead (Owens and Randhawa, 2004, p. 417). This non-interventionist approach was appreciated by the service's traditional patients – white middle-class people – but the nurses found it hard to put into practice when they were hampered by language differences. In addition, some South Asian patients did not understand the philosophy, and expected the nurses to take charge. Consequently, standing back resulted in people's needs not being met, and 'it was recognised by some [nurses] that "cultural competence" may require a more interventionist and persistent approach to the provision of care services than philosophies of palliative care usually allow' (Owens and Randhawa, 2004, p. 417).

1.3 Categorising difference

Understanding and meeting the needs of diverse groups is important, but it is not easy to categorise and describe people's differences. For one thing, there can be important variations within categories. For example, Gypsy Travellers can be Irish, Welsh, Scottish or English, all sharing some aspects of cultural identity and yet having different languages. The broad category 'Asian' includes people with different religions, languages and regional backgrounds. Similarly, the term 'disabled children' covers a wide range of impairments and circumstances.

Equally, placing emphasis on differences can draw attention away from things that people share in common. As you read in Resource 13, a black child who uses sign language, for instance, may feel more at home with a white carer who can sign than with a black carer who can't.

A third difficulty is that categorising people can exaggerate difference. Taking ethnicity as an example, Yasmin Gunaratnam (2001a) argues that the term 'ethnic minorities' conveys the idea that some people's cultural practices are exotic, strange and problematic. This sets up a 'them and us' mentality, as expressed by one of the white palliative care nurses in the study by Owens and Randhawa:

> ... although I can try to, sort of, empathise with them, it's very different from my culture; they're very different.

(Quoted in Owens and Randhawa, 2004, p. 418)

Meanwhile, the culture of the 'majority' group – in this case White British – is seen as 'undifferentiated and unproblematic' (Gunaratnam, 2001a, p. 304).

Activity 3   White culture

Allow about 5 minutes

Jot down some examples that you feel describe the culture of someone whose ethnic group is described as 'White British'.

Comment

Someone who tested this course wrote:

> I found this really difficult and in the end based my answer on my parents who are in their 80s. My dad has various routines which he likes to stick to wherever he is. He likes to eat a cooked breakfast (bacon and eggs); make a daily visit to the pub (half a pint of best bitter); and on Christmas Day he expects to eat 'turkey and all the trimmings'. My mum, on the other hand, is a bit more 'middle class' in her outlook and prefers to drink wine. She's also Scottish and likes to celebrate Hogmanay in style.

Another person said:

> I took my white Yorkshire dad to look at various care homes. Almost all were out of the question because of a prevailing culture of loud TV and forced bonhomie. He hated group outings and singalongs. He was a quiet, bookish man; a devout Methodist. His only remaining pleasure was walking – which most care homes didn't allow except under supervision.

Your response is likely to be influenced by your own ethnicity and culture, and whether you identify yourself as 'White British'. It may be easier to come up with examples if you are not from this ethnic group. If you are White British, it might have been difficult to describe what white culture is because you may never have thought before about what this means. You might also have queried what 'British' means, and how it compares with being Irish, Welsh, Scottish or English. As the course testers pointed out, differences based on class and religion also play a part in a person's culture.

Activity 3 underlines two points:

- that 'white' culture is usually taken for granted and is what the mainstream of UK life caters for
- there is no single form of any culture – 'culture' depends on factors such as social class, age, religion and regional background.

As Gunaratnam (2001a) suggests, the majority ethnic group's culture is usually seen as the norm. To people from other groups, however, it is likely to seem strange. Here is an extract from advice about British social behaviour, offered to young people who want to move to the UK to study:

> The social behaviour you will experience in Britain may be very different to your own culture. Some examples include:
>
> […]
>
> - British people are usually very polite, using 'please' and 'thank-you' a lot, which you may not be used to. In addition, the British have a tendency to be very self critical and apologetic. You will find that the words 'sorry' and 'excuse me' are also used frequently

- The British often have difficulty saying what they really mean, for example refusing a request, or making a critical comment, for fear of causing offence or upset …

[…]

- Maintaining eye contact in the UK is generally seen as a sign of sincerity, while in some cultures an avoidance of eye contact is seen as a mark of respect

(Independent Schools Council, undated)

Did you recognise these aspects of social behaviour as particular to 'Britishness'?

1.4 Communities of identity

Unit 10 introduced the idea of 'communities of identity'. These are based on shared characteristics such as ethnic origin, religion, politics, sexual orientation, impairments or long-term conditions (Willmott, 1989).

Identity communities offer a sense of belonging which is not necessarily based on where people live. Indeed, identity communities often cut across geographical boundaries. Allan Sutherland, who has epilepsy, remembers an 'extraordinary and emotional weekend' he spent with other disabled people in the early days of the disability movement:

> I arrived there not calling myself disabled. I hadn't met other disabled people. I hadn't, in 20 years of living with epilepsy, ever met anyone I knew to have my own disability. That weekend, I found acceptance and a disabled identity.
>
> … To suddenly find [myself] with other like-minded disabled people, to suddenly be part of a group of disabled people was absolutely mind-blowing.

(Sutherland, 2006, p. 3)

Alison Gilchrist (2004) suggests that communities of identity develop when people come together in the face of adversity. Patrice Van Cleemput and her colleagues found that Gypsy Travellers feel rejected and threatened by the mainstream of society. One of them told the researchers:

> It is frightening being a Traveller love, because no-one wants you … if they could, they'd build a hole and they'd shove all the Travellers into it and they'd just bury them all there. If there was no law they would do that

(Van Cleemput et al., 2004, p. 15)

In response to this experience:

> Gypsy Travellers … maintain their separateness and … attempt to continue their traditional lifestyle despite the threats. This appears to reinforce their cohesion as an ethnic group.

(Van Cleemput et al., 2004, p. 15)

Shared identity can generate an important source of support for people whose perspectives are excluded, marginalised or hidden in the mainstream of community life. For example, in Block 2, Owen and Mick found support among other men with haemophilia who were HIV-positive. The organisations with which they became involved had sprung up to create a sense of solidarity among men who were HIV-positive, in the face of public hostility. However, joining the support groups was not easy for Owen and Mick because it required them to embrace identities which – at the time – were stigmatising and provoked anti-gay prejudices in the wider community.

Communities of identity are based on shared experience, and offer a sense of solidarity and belonging

Activity 4   Identities and disadvantage

Allow about 10 minutes

(a) Look at the photographs above, which show people who have come together because of their shared experience. What community of identity does each picture represent?

(b) Now choose just one picture, and think of an example of adversity faced by people who belong to this group. How might this group of people be disadvantaged in relation to their health and social care needs, or in gaining access to services?

Comment

(a) The first photo shows disabled men who have come together as a team to play sport. The two lesbian women in the second photo are part of the wider gay and lesbian community. The third and fourth both show different groups of people who nonetheless share something in common on the basis of their age. You may also have noticed that each picture suggests more than one identity community. The people in the pictures are not just 'disabled', 'lesbian', 'young' and 'older': they might also feel a sense of shared identity on the basis of gender and ethnicity.

(b) There are many possible answers, depending on the photo you chose, but here are some suggestions.

- **Examples of adversity**:

  Disabled people often find it difficult to access appropriate training and employment, with negative effects on their income.

  Lesbians and gay men still conceal their sexuality in some situations, for fear of risking hostility and exclusion.

  Young people – and especially young black people – are affected by negative images portrayed in the media. This influences the way they are treated in their neighbourhoods; for example, being 'moved on' by the police.

  Older people who rely on state pensions have low incomes.

- **Ways in which people might be disadvantaged**:

  Disabled people will find their quality of life restricted if they use social care services that don't fully meet their needs.

  In hospital, gay men and lesbians often find that their partners are not recognised as next of kin.

  Young people don't always know how to access health care, or lack the confidence to seek advice. If you work in childcare services, you may have noticed that young black people are over-represented in the care system.

  Older people are not always offered the same choices and quality of health care as working-age people.

  People from minority ethnic groups often lack information about obtaining home care (or health care), especially if they don't speak much English.

Communities of identity can be a resource through which disadvantaged people can find support. The photos you have just been looking at show people who value their difference and are proud to be part of an identity community, but behind each picture is a story of disadvantage, inequality and discrimination.

This section has explored the implications of diversity in relation to people using health and social care services. You have seen that diversity is complex because neither people nor their needs can be neatly categorised. So does this imply that health and social care services should take no account of difference? No, but it does suggest that an over-simplistic approach will not be helpful. You will have the opportunity to develop your understanding of these ideas as you progress through the rest of this unit.

Key points

- Valuing diversity is about welcoming variety and difference; it also involves recognising that differences can lead to inequalities in life chances and in access to care provision.
- 'Treating everyone the same' won't meet everyone's needs: care workers and care providers need to recognise that people have particular needs which arise from their diversity.
- However, seeing people only as 'different' ignores the commonalities between groups, and the diversity within them.
- Difference – in the sense of shared identity – can be a source of strength and support for care service users.

2 Stereotypes, prejudices and discrimination, and their impact on care

There were a number of examples in Unit 10 where people's lives have been affected by other people's assumptions about them. Lynsey Hanley, in Chapter 10 in the Reader, writes about the media portrayal of council tenants as 'failures'. Simon, who has mental health problems and talks constantly to himself as if hearing voices, was excluded from the community centre because people thought of him as 'dangerous'. These labels and assumptions are known as 'stereotypes'. This section begins by exploring the nature of stereotypes and their implications for care.

2.1 Stereotypes

First, read about Mhàiri, a disabled woman who lives with her partner Gillian.

Mhàiri

Mhàiri, a white Scottish woman in her early sixties, had a stroke six months ago. Although close to retirement, she'd initially intended to return to her job as a store manager. However, this has proved impossible as she hasn't recovered as well as she'd hoped. The stroke affected Mhàiri's vision and she can't drive her car. As she finds it difficult to walk, she is dependent on her partner Gillian to take her places. She doesn't like having to rely so much on Gillian.

Mhàiri's doctor suggests putting her name forward to be assessed for a wheelchair. Although Mhàiri says she will consider this, she leaves the surgery feeling very distressed. She thinks about it over the next few days, but somehow can't accept the mental image of herself in a wheelchair. 'I'm just not that kind of person', she tells Gillian.

When Mhàiri reacted against the idea of being in a wheelchair, one of her concerns might have been how it would change the way she sees herself, and is seen by others. Researcher Bob Sapey and his colleagues asked wheelchair users about the attitudes they experienced from professionals and other people who didn't use wheelchairs. One participant explained:

> It's like when you go to the hospital or the doctors, if you go with anybody because you're in a wheelchair they don't address you, they look over you and that really infuriates me.

(Sapey et al., 2005, p. 494)

This person had found that using a wheelchair led to being ignored, apparently on the assumption that they were not in control of the situation, or were unable to understand things.

The assumptions made about people in wheelchairs are an example of generalisations known as stereotypes. The next activity explores the effects of stereotyping through an extract from Allan Sutherland's book, *Disabled We Stand*, written in 1982 during the early days of the disabled people's movement.

Resources

Activity 5 Stereotypes of disabled people

Allow about 50 minutes

(a) Read Resource 14, 'Stereotypes of disability', by Allan Sutherland. As you do so, note down some examples of stereotypes about disabled people.

(b) Make some notes about the consequences of these stereotypes for disabled people.

(c) What do you think care workers could do to counter the effects of stereotypes? (A few suggestions are made in the extract.)

Comment

(a) There were too many examples to list them all here, but one I noted was that people in wheelchairs are seen either as helpless and incapable ('deaf, dumb and stupid'), or as having some kind of super-human qualities. Another stereotype was that people with speech difficulties are deaf ('Because I've got a speech defect, people tend to shout').

(b) The extract suggests that stereotyping affects disabled people in a number of ways:

- Stereotypes can act as 'self-fulfilling prophecies'; for example, assuming that a disabled person cannot communicate results in not listening to them properly.

- Stereotypes can also result in a failure to consult disabled people about what support they need, with the consequence that so-called 'help' is misdirected and inappropriate.

- Stereotypes have the effect of depersonalising people. In other words, people are not seen as individuals. The complexity of their personalities is ignored, and their needs are seen in simplistic terms. This is true even when stereotypes appear to be positive.

(c) The extract suggests several things that care workers can do to counter the effects of stereotyping, and you may have added your own ideas too:

- Care workers need to keep an open mind and get to know the person as an individual.

- If care workers are unable to understand a person's speech, they need to be patient and listen carefully until they are familiar with that person's method of communicating. From your own experience, you might also have mentioned learning to use communication aids, such as sign language.

- Care workers need to recognise service users' abilities; for example, they should communicate directly with disabled people, even when they are accompanied by carers, and should avoid 'talking down' to all service users.

- Care workers should also ask disabled people what assistance they would like, instead of attempting to 'act for' people.

Did you add any other suggestions?

Relying on stereotyped assumptions can result in inappropriate offers of help

Rather than confuse you with a whole bunch of directions, why don't I just show this map to your dog.

A stereotype, then, is a commonly held set of assumptions about someone, based on the perceived characteristics of a particular group to which they belong (an ethnic or religious group, for example). Stereotypes present an oversimplified and inaccurate view, not based on knowledge of the individual in question.

We cannot avoid using stereotypes in everyday life. They act as a kind of shorthand to help us make sense of the complex world around us. We can't treat everyone as an individual all the time. For example, a social care service could not organise services for older people without making some assumptions about what they have in common. But it's important to be aware of the impact of stereotypes, because they can have damaging consequences for individuals.

The problem with stereotypes is that they distort how people are seen. Robina Shah observes:

> … once they are formed, stereotypes lead individuals to assume that all members of a racial, ethnic, religious or other group, possess similar traits or act in the same manner. In short, stereotypes lead persons who hold them to ignore important differences between unique individuals.

(Shah, 1995, p. 17)

In Resource 14, Sutherland cites Micheline Mason who points out that stereotypes are not necessarily negative. However, they can still have depersonalising implications: by 'summing up a person's whole character in terms of their disability it robs them of their individuality' (Resource 14, p. 75).

Amy, a young woman describing herself as 'half Romany', expresses her frustration at the depersonalising effects of stereotypes about Gypsy Travellers:

[*People who are non-Gypsies]

> … it seems like the gaujas[*] have two stereo types: one is that Gypsies (who live in modern caravans) are thieves and they're dirty etc. and the other is that Gypsies still live in the pretty little caravans like they have for 'hundreds of years' and live idyllic care-free lives wandering from place to place selling flowers.

[…]

A lot of gaujas can't seem to realise that they are only stereotypes and they're not true, and some gaujas think that the 'old style' Gypsies are the only real Romanies and if you live in a metal caravan you're not a Romany.

It annoys me when gaujas think that Gypsies are just anyone who lives in a caravan, and if you don't you can't be one.

(BBC, undated)

The long-standing stereotype that 'Gypsies are dirty' is particularly inaccurate, as Gypsy Traveller culture has strict rules about cleanliness and hygiene. Anna Lee explains:

We never wash in a sink. If we have a sink in the trailer it's always got a dish inside, 'cos we have separate bowls for everything … for washing up … for washing our hands and face … and for wiping around. We never get 'em mixed up. When we are doing our laundry we won't wash our tea towels in with all the rest of our clothes, 'cos we think that's very unclean.

(Quoted in Bristol City Council, 2006, p. 6)

Today, Gypsy Travellers' caravans are of modern design

It is not only service users who are affected by stereotyped generalisations. A commonplace stereotype is that 'women are the carers in families'. You might remember how in Unit 1, Ann didn't feel she had any choice about giving up paid work to care for Angus: she saw this as 'a woman's job'. Her views were based on her own experience of family life, but they also reflect traditional stereotypical assumptions.

Two frequently held stereotypes about South Asian people are that 'they live in extended close-knit families', and that 'they care for their own' and therefore do not want or need care services. However, research evidence indicates that this generalisation is misleading:

Even though there is evidence of increased levels of extended family involvement by Pakistani and Bangladeshi families, only a quarter of such families reported receiving 'a lot of help' from family members (Chamba et al., 1999). It is not clear whether these somewhat raised rates of informal help are the *cause* or rather the *result* of the absence of formal services. Other assumptions, for example, that minority families do not like to send their children to respite care facilities, also seem, on the evidence, to be a reflection of the perceived lack of trust that the service provided will be appropriate to the needs of their children (and will not expose them to overt racism), rather than a cultural preference.

(Fazil et al., 2002, p. 239)

Stereotypes about gender and ethnicity can lead to unrealistic expectations of individual women's availability or willingness to take on a carer's role, which in turn can mean that support for service users and informal carers is inadequate, or may not even be offered.

2.2 Avoiding stereotypes

We return now to Mhàiri. You have seen the common generalisations made about disabled people, but what other stereotypes might be imposed on her? In certain situations she could find that assumptions are made in connection with her age and gender (a woman in her sixties), her nationality (Scottish) and her sexuality (lesbian). We explore this last one in the next part of Mhàiri's story.

Activity 6   More assumptions about Mhàiri

Allow about 10 minutes

Read the next part of Mhàiri's story and answer the questions that follow.

> ### Mhàiri's care assessment
>
> Mhàiri has decided to ask for some personal care in the home. This is quite a big step, but she finds it difficult to get out of bed, and get washed and dressed. Until now, she has either struggled to do this by herself (and then been too exhausted to do anything once she is up) or relied on Gillian to help her. However, Gillian has been promoted and needs to start work earlier, and in any case Mhàiri is very reluctant for Gillian to be involved in her personal care.
>
> Stuart, a care manager from the local social services office, visits Mhàiri to assess her care needs. As part of the assessment he asks her if she is married; Mhàiri hesitates and then tells him she is divorced, but that she lives with Gillian. Stuart assumes that Gillian is just a lodger or a friend, and Mhàiri – who has chosen not 'come out' as a lesbian to her family or her doctor – goes along with his assumption. A home care worker is allocated for an hour each morning. Sometimes it's Kirsty, at other times it's Janet. Mhàiri arranges for them to have a key and let themselves in after Gillian has left for work. Things begin reasonably well, until one day Janet arrives very early and is taken aback to find both Mhàiri and Gillian in the bed. Overcome with embarrassment and confusion, she doesn't know what to do and rushes out of the house.

(a) What stereotypes do you think are influencing Stuart's perceptions about Mhàiri?

(b) How could this situation have been avoided?

Comment

(a) There may be several stereotypes at work here. First, there is the assumption that disabled people (and older people) don't have sexual feelings, and second, that if they do have any kind of sexuality, they are assumed to be heterosexual. Finally, another common stereotype which applies here is that if you have been married, you are not gay or lesbian.

(b) It might have been easier for Mhàiri to be open about Gillian if Stuart had used more neutral language when asking about her relationships (referring to a 'partner' rather than being 'married'). However, perhaps the main difficulty was not just to do with language, but to do with stereotyped assumptions. Mhàiri did try to explain about Gillian, but perhaps because Stuart wasn't expecting her to be anything other than heterosexual, he automatically took the phrase 'living with' to mean they were just friends. Stuart could have listened more carefully and open-mindedly to what Mhàiri was trying to tell him.

Perhaps Stuart's mistake is understandable. Stereotypes are so commonplace that they can't be banished entirely. However, in care work it is very important to question our own assumptions. The Royal College of Nursing, in conjunction with Unison, has produced some guidance for staff working with lesbian and gay service users. This includes a checklist which would have been helpful for Stuart:

- Be aware that you have lesbian, gay and bisexual service users, even if you don't know who they are.
- Be sensitive about the way you request information from service users, using language which is inclusive and gender neutral.

[…]

- Make it safe for same sex partners and family members to be open about their relationships if they want to, so they can be supported during illness or crisis.
- Respect privacy and confidentiality.
- If necessary, provide lesbian, gay and bisexual service users and their families with details of where to get further, specialist support, advice and information.

(Royal College of Nursing and UNISON, undated)

Research indicates that older people are generally assumed to be either asexual or heterosexual. This stereotype is reinforced because many older gay men and lesbians have grown up concealing their private lives (Price, 2005), not least because male homosexuality was illegal in the UK before 1967, and lesbian relationships, although never officially illegal, were equally disapproved of. When older gay men and lesbians need care, their privacy is compromised:

> … the onset of disability in later life may be a minefield of potential 'outings'. … previously private matters can suddenly be open to public scrutiny. A person's domestic arrangements and individual living circumstances may be observed and judged in a negative light by those who provide care or treatment or who may visit the home for the purpose of assessment. … for older gay men and lesbians who may have lived a lifetime 'passing' as heterosexual, this may compound already high levels of stress and anxiety.

(Price, 2005, p. 17)

As Resource 14 pointed out, stereotypes can be either positive or negative, although the word has come to be associated mainly with negative meanings. When stereotypes are used unthinkingly as the basis for providing care, people's individuality is diminished, and they can be denied the opportunity to express their personalities and needs. Activities 5 and 6 have suggested ways in which care workers can resist relying on stereotypes as the basis for offering services. Summarising these, you have seen that care workers need to try to keep an open mind, and *be prepared to question their own assumptions* drawn from everyday stereotypes. As you saw in Section 1, it is important to recognise people's cultural, religious and other particular needs. However, this by itself is no substitute for finding out about service users as individuals, taking account of both diversity and individual preferences.

2.3 Prejudice

You have seen that making stereotypical assumptions can lead to people not being provided with appropriate care. A further problem with broad generalisations is that they can lead to prejudiced beliefs. A prejudice is a judgement made in advance about a person, on the basis of stereotyped assumptions. Whereas a stereotype may simply be a shorthand (even if thoughtless and superficial) way of 'labelling' someone, a prejudice goes beyond description to a belief about whether the assumed characteristics are positive or negative. For example, the inaccurate stereotype that 'Gypsies are dirty' may give rise to the negative prejudice: 'I don't like Gypsies because they are dirty'.

Just as everybody uses stereotypes to help make sense of complex information, we all tend to hold prejudices (even though we may not recognise or act on them). Stonewall, an organisation which promotes equality for lesbians, gay men and bisexuals, commissioned an opinion poll to find out about people's prejudices and what influences them. Stonewall found that:

> Almost two-thirds of people in England (64%) can name at least one minority group towards whom they feel less positive – representing 25 million adults across the country. The most frequently cited are **travellers/gypsies** (35%), and **refugees/asylum seekers** (34%), while around one in five (18%) mentions an **ethnic group** towards which they feel less positive, and one in six (17%) cites **gay or lesbian people**.

> (Stonewall, undated)

Stonewall also found that people cited a number of stereotypes to justify their prejudices; for example, that Gypsy Travellers don't pay taxes, don't respect private property, and are 'unsightly, dirty or unhygienic' (Valentine and McDonald, 2004, p. 12).

In care work, prejudice has a detrimental effect on people's experiences of seeking and receiving services. Research commissioned by the Department for Work and Pensions (DWP) revealed that gay and lesbian disabled people are disadvantaged by a variety of prejudiced beliefs. For example, a disabled lesbian felt that she was seen as somehow 'unnatural' or abnormal:

> … society does not look at disabled people as sexual beings … if you're disabled they don't expect you to have sexuality or want a physical relationship … They don't think you're capable, they sometimes don't

> feel you have emotions and feelings like everyone else, for a disabled person to be sexual *and* a lesbian, then God, that is outrageous!

(Female, 46, lesbian, white, mobility impairment)

(Quoted in Molloy et al., 2003, p. 54)

The impact of such prejudices in health care can be subtle. In the report by Molloy et al., it wasn't that people received a lower standard of treatment in a physical sense, more that they were made to feel uncomfortable:

> You can see their faces sometimes – next of kin, right, and I put [partner's name] down and they sort of look at you – what relationship is she … you get the looks … from the nurses and other patients and stuff like that.

(Female, 49, lesbian, white, mental impairment)

(Quoted in Molloy et al., 2003, p. 123)

In other cases, service users felt that hostile attitudes spilled over into the quality of care they received:

> She [the nurse] was so rough, and I'm sure that was because of my sexuality. … it was a really horrible experience … and it's really put – you know, it really did shake me up.

(Female, 27, lesbian, white, cognitive impairment)

(Quoted in Molloy et al., 2003, p. 123)

Gypsy Travellers report how prejudice within the health service restricts their access to doctors, with receptionists being considered hostile or unsympathetic:

> you can tell in a second, you can tell by their attitude, they don't look you in the eye …
>
> the receptionists are harder to get past … I think they're doing the doctor a favour … 'I did something good today, I kept the Gypsies away'.

(Quoted in Van Cleemput et al., 2004, p. 70)

Do you remember Simon, in Unit 10, who experienced hostility and exclusion because of his mental health? Since 1993, the Department of Health has carried out three-yearly surveys of public attitudes towards people with mental health problems. The 2007 survey revealed that, in England, there had been an increase in prejudice over the previous ten years, including a rise in the percentage of people who thought that people with mental health problems are 'prone to violence' (TNS for Shift, CSIP, 2007). Prejudice not only has a detrimental effect on the people who currently use services, it also discourages others who need help. Paul Farmer, Chief Executive of Mind, points out:

> The cost of stigma is high. It prevents many people with mental health problems from living normal lives, and it deters people from seeking help when they need it.
>
> … It's crucial, for their own wellbeing, that … people are confident discussing mental health problems with their peers, without the fear of stigma.

(Quoted in Mind, 2007)

Prejudices can become ingrained and hard to shake off, because as Shah observes:

> … persons who are prejudiced tend to notice and only remember certain kinds of information about the groups they dislike – 'facts that are largely negative in nature'.

(Shah, 1995, p. 17)

Attitudes can be changed, however. In Scotland, public attitudes towards people with mental health problems have begun to be more tolerant. This is considered to be the result of a well-resourced anti-stigma campaign funded by the Scottish Government:

> In three years from 2002 to 2005, the proportion of people in Scotland saying people with mental health problems are often dangerous fell from 32 per cent to 15 per cent, a drop of around half, compared to a 17 per cent increase in the belief in England that people with mental health problems are prone to violence.

(Mind, 2007)

As you have seen, we can all fall back on stereotypes and hold prejudiced views (even though we try to resist them). The next activity helps you to consider this in relation to yourself.

Activity 7   What stereotypes and prejudices do you hold?

Allow about 5 minutes

Anyone can have stereotyped perceptions and hold prejudiced views. Think about any stereotypes and prejudices that you hold, even if you try not to act on them, and jot down a note about this.

Comment

How did you get on? While writing this block, I've realised that I visualise doctors as male. This is a stereotype which persists, despite my being registered with a woman GP.

So, to sum up:

*   Stereotypes are oversimplified and distorted perceptions.
*   Prejudices are negative attitudes or beliefs based on inaccurate and misleading stereotypes.

Anyone can hold these views, but in care work, it's important to step back and reflect on the stereotypes and prejudices that affect our thinking. If we are aware of them, we are less likely to act on them.

2.4 Discrimination

When prejudiced beliefs are acted upon, this becomes discrimination. Shah clarifies the distinction between prejudice and discrimination like this:

> … prejudice generally refers to negative attitudes … discrimination describes negative actions directed against the persons who are its objects – the victims of prejudice.

(Shah, 1995, p. 17)

In Chapter 10 in the Reader, Lynsey Hanley gives an example of the relationship between stereotypes, prejudices and discrimination. She argues that seeing all council estate residents as 'failures' (stereotype) gives rise to the belief that they don't value education and that the children are not interested in academic success (prejudice).

In Hanley's experience, this resulted in teachers steering young people towards 'dead end' jobs instead of pursuing higher education or other qualifications (discrimination).

To take another case, African Caribbean families are often seen in a stereotyped way as 'virtually non-existent as a unit or rapidly falling apart, with mothers being seen as too strong and committed to wage-earning' (Ahmed, quoted in Thompson, 2006, p. 77). Jo Haynes and colleagues found that children from dual heritage White/Black Caribbean families were assumed to live in single-parent households with a white mother, even when the majority were living with both parents (Haynes et al., 2006).

In this context:

- African Caribbean fathers are stereotyped as 'absent' and 'uninvolved'.
- This can lead to the prejudiced view that they are not good fathers.
- When acted upon, such prejudices may result in discriminatory care practice.

For example, professionals have ignored black fathers when working with families and young children:

> ... fathers are often excluded from any consultation or participation on service development and are a group in need of engagement. For example [a 1998] study showed how stereotypical views of black fathers affected health visitors' perception of their role in their child's development.

> (Bignall and Box, 2002, p. 5)

Recent studies have raised awareness of how older people are discriminated against in health care. This need not be intentionally unfair, but can occur in the course of everyday practice. The Open University's Research on Age Discrimination Project (RoAD) asked people about their experiences of age-related prejudices. Here's a social worker's account of what can happen when stereotypes and prejudices are translated into discriminatory actions:

> I was working in a community mental health team for older people when I was asked to assess a gentleman (in his 70s) who had taken to his bed because of severe depression. The GP commented that there was nothing that could be done as 'his time had come'. I arranged for the gentleman to see a psychiatrist who recommended an admission to a psychiatric hospital. Three weeks later the gentleman returned to the community and was able to take up all activities of daily living.

> (Quoted in Bytheway et al., 2007, p. 43)

Care workers are frequently in a position where they need to make judgements about people: assessing someone's needs for a service; finding out about their health and their routines when they come into residential care or hospital; and generally responding to day-to-day care situations. The case studies and examples in this section have highlighted the importance of looking beyond stereotyped assumptions. When stereotypes and prejudice are acted upon, this leads to discrimination.

Key points

- It is important for care workers and providers to recognise people's cultural, religious and other preferences, but equally important that they try to avoid making assumptions based on stereotypes rather than knowledge of the individual.
- Stereotyped perceptions can lead people to hold prejudiced beliefs.
- When prejudiced beliefs are acted upon, this becomes discrimination, and results in inappropriate and poor-quality care for service users.

Learning skills: Helping your memory by making structured notes

Reader

At the end of Unit 10, you read about the way your memory works by using structures and patterns to organise what's in your head and link it all together. Have you tried to make any use of this in the way you are approaching Unit 11? Have you tried making structured notes to link ideas together? You can see some examples of how this can be done by reading Section 6.4 of *The Good Study Guide* (pages 148–53). Then you can think about whether to try a different way of making notes on this unit.

3 Experiencing discrimination

This section considers discrimination in relation to service users and care workers, with a focus on ethnicity. It begins with the true story of a black health care worker. However, the organisational issues to be discussed here are relevant for service users and workers from any ethnic background, or from any other minority group.

3.1 An example of racial discrimination

In 2004, Rosie Purves, a black nurse, won a racial discrimination claim against her employer.

> **Nurse wins £20,000 in race case**
>
> A black nurse suffered racial discrimination when she was banned from taking care of a sick white baby, an employment tribunal ruled yesterday.
>
> Rosie Purves, 58, brought the case against Southampton University Hospitals NHS Trust for race discrimination … after managers moved the six-month-old girl to a different ward.
>
> (Press Association, 2004)

> Tribunal chairman Martin Kurrein told the hearing on Monday that the child's mother admitted she had 'no problem' with the care that Mrs Purves had provided but she was 'a racist' and did not want a black person to care for her child.
>
> Mr Kurrein said the trust was 'effectively silent and complicit in the racist demands' made by the child's mother.
>
> He added: 'It was extremely hurtful for the applicant to be excluded from caring for a child simply on the basis of the colour of her skin.'
>
> (BBC News, 2004)

The case of Rosie Purves was reported in the national press, but the Reader chapter you are going to read is in her own words.

Reader

Activity 8   What is racism?

Allow about 40 minutes

Turn to Chapter 3, 'Racist abuse ruined my life', by Rosie Purves in the Reader (pages 23–5).

(a) First, read the article and note down one or two examples of actions which you think are racist in some way.

(b) Now look at your notes and use them to write a short description of what you think racism involves – how would you describe it?

(c) What effect did these incidents have on Rosie's life?

Comment

(a) The most obvious examples of racist actions were:

- when the first mother said she didn't want her child to be looked after by Rosie because she was black

- when the two other mothers spoke abusively to Rosie (referring to her ethnicity and skin colour), both in the hospital and at the school.

(b) In these examples, racism involved behaving offensively towards someone on account of their ethnic group (and in this case, Rosie's skin colour was part of her ethnicity).

In part (a), you might have noted one or more of the following as racism:

- when Rosie's colleagues just went along with the consultant

- when the consultant paediatrician agreed with the mother's request and ordered the staff to move the child

- when the NHS Trust failed to take any action to challenge the consultant or the mother.

Is it fair to call the last three examples racism? Rosie's colleagues were, she says, just doing what they had been told to do; and the consultant's actions were motivated by an attempt to prioritise the patient and support the mother's choice. It might be argued that the individuals concerned didn't actually hold racist views or intend to act harmfully towards Rosie. These actions, therefore, were more to do with the position taken by the employing organisation. As for the hospital, its response made it appear that the mother's objection was reasonable. In other words, it appeared to endorse racism. And by singling out Rosie to be treated differently on account of her ethnic group, it was actively operating in a racist way. So it could be argued that, even if individual employees didn't have racist intentions, they were participating in the institution's racism.

(c) Rosie's life changed for the worse in many ways. People who tested this activity pointed out the following:

- Rosie found herself being treated differently from other nurses for no other reason than her skin colour, while the mother who had been openly racist towards her was treated as perfectly normal, and got just what she wanted.

- Rosie's colleagues didn't support her – in fact their silence made it appear as if they agreed that she was the problem, not the mother's racism. So she felt isolated and became depressed, feeling she had no one to turn to. Rosie didn't talk to her family or anyone else because she felt ashamed at the way she'd been treated – even though she hadn't done anything wrong and what had happened wasn't her fault.

- Rosie felt singled out and discriminated against for reasons that were nothing to do with her or her capabilities, but simply to do with racial prejudice.

Rosie was prevented from carrying out her job when the white child was moved to a different ward. This was purely on account of her skin colour – the mother was explicit that the reason she didn't want Rosie near her child was because she was black. (One of the news reports quoted above confirms that the mother had 'no problem' with the care Rosie had provided.) This is a clear example of racism on the white mother's part. Indeed, she had proclaimed herself as a racist. But it is also an example of the actions of an institution (the hospital) being racist. You will be coming back to this point later.

3.2 Dealing with racism

Rosie took no action for seven years, which is a very long time to live with the effects of such a distressing incident. What made it so difficult for Rosie and her colleagues to do anything to prevent this happening?

Reader

Activity 9 Why did this happen?

Allow about 10 minutes

Look at Chapter 3 of the Reader again, and this time jot down your thoughts in response to the following questions:

(a) Why do you think it took Rosie so long to complain?

(b) Why do you think her nurse colleagues didn't intervene to support her?

(c) Why do you think senior hospital staff went along with the mother's demands?

Comment

The answers to these questions are discussed below, so keep your notes to one side and add to them as you read through the rest of this section.

Rosie knew she was good at her job, so she was horrified to find that the hospital agreed with the mother and treated her so unfairly. She writes that feelings of shock and shame prevented her from talking about what had happened, and so she just 'went along with it'. Why was this?

The Reader chapter suggests several factors that made it difficult for Rosie and her colleagues to challenge these racist incidents. In a discussion of racism in health care, Gunaratnam writes that:

> … dealing with racism [can] be subverted by a number of different factors, including:
>
> - An organizational 'culture of niceness' that suppresses confrontation of racism
>
> - Fear and anxiety associated with talking about or discussing racism
>
> [...]
>
> - A lack of clear organizational policy on such issues as racial harassment

(Gunaratnam, 2000, p. 148)

These factors form a useful framework for analysing Rosie Purves' experience. Below, we will consider all three points, beginning with the lack of a clear policy.

Lack of a clear policy

One of the reasons it was hard for Rosie and her colleagues – including the consultant – to know what to do is that their employer didn't seem to have any written guidelines for dealing with such situations. The school, on the other hand, appears to have had a clearer policy about discrimination. When Rosie, in her additional role as school nurse, complained about the way she was being treated, the head of department:

> … called the family in straightaway for a meeting. He was very stern and said if there was any more abuse at the school the child would be asked to leave.

(Reader, Chapter 3, p. 24)

Equal opportunities policies are useful in setting out explicitly what racial harassment means and what the organisation intends to do about it. But do written policies actually prevent racism and other kinds of discrimination, or can they be just a paper exercise? In 2005, 80–90% of organisations had written equality policies, although within the NHS the percentage was considerably smaller (Bhavnani et al., 2005, p. 82). However, Claire Chambers and Obrey Alexis (2004) argue that there can be a 'reality gap' between what written policies say and what actually takes place in an organisation.

Gunaratnam agrees that written policies make it easier to talk about racism, and deal with it, but emphasises that they are no substitute for actually discussing racism – and the difficulties of dealing with it – in the workplace:

> Equal opportunity policies have a vital role to play … but real change can only be accomplished by the development of an organizational culture and climate that not only empowers staff to speak out, but also recognizes that working towards race equality can feel threatening.

(Gunaratnam, 2000, p. 148)

Although there are limitations on what equal opportunities policies can achieve, it would have helped Rosie and her colleagues if they had been able to refer to one.

Fear of challenging the organisational climate

Every workplace has its own organisational 'culture' or 'climate', which consists of informal and unwritten expectations ('norms') about what people can do and say. One of the course testers suggested that it took Rosie such a long time to complain because:

> She may have worried about coming forward and 'making a fuss' – and she might have feared she would only make things worse for herself. If the assumption seems to be that racial discrimination is 'normal' and not even worth talking about, it's very hard for just one person to take a stand and challenge this.

Moving the child to a different part of the hospital didn't deal with the racism; it simply covered it up and, as Rosie says, made it seem acceptable. In this working climate, the other staff went along with the consultant's orders to move the child to another part of the ward. This made it even harder for Rosie to complain, because she had no support from her colleagues or manager.

Difficulty in talking about racism

It was also difficult for Rosie to do anything because although her colleagues felt uncomfortable about what had happened, nobody said anything: it remained, as she says, 'an unspoken thing'.

Ignoring or suppressing concerns about racism doesn't just affect care workers: if staff feel unable to talk about racism, they will not be able to challenge it when it is directed against service users. In the next activity, you can read another real-life account of racism, this time against hospital patients.

Activity 10   Talking about racism

Allow about 10 minutes

Read this account told by Roz, a white nurse.

Roz's dilemma (Part 1)

Roz: … It was the patient's wife who made racist comments and the patient never said 'yea' or 'nay'. And they were both white and then he, he was admitted into a bay that had three, um, three black men. Two from Jamaica and one from Ghana and, um she made loud racist comments that she thought it was disgusting that her husband should be in a bay with three black men on their own.

Kate: (gasps).

[…]

Roz: … one was in his 50s and the two other were late 60s and … both … I think chose to let it wash over them. But the chap who was in his 50s was rightly angry about it and … I felt incredibly embarrassed about it. I felt, really, really dreadful about it and this woman was making loud comments about 'how these dark people come in all loud during the day and night and they're noisy and they bring in smelly food' … He was angry at her and at her attitude.

(Quoted in Gunaratnam, 2001b, p. 72)

What would you do in her place? When you have jotted down your thoughts, read on and compare your response with what Roz actually did.

In the next extract, Roz concludes her story and explains what actually happened.

Roz's dilemma (Part 2)

Roz: … we had a big debate about whether this white bloke should be moved into a, a side room and I felt I didn't want my other patients to be exposed to his wife but I also felt that was giving his wife exactly what she wanted. So in the end … I went and spoke with the chap who was in his 50s …

[…]

I actually went and picked his brains about it and he said 'No'. He felt that that man should stay there and that they would cope with it and the other three blokes were really supportive. And I think I learnt a lot about that and it also made me feel less frightened of actually discussing racism with, with people who aren't white because, I think I've always been embarrassed to sort of discuss it before, because I felt so shameful, so responsible for it.

(Quoted in Gunaratnam, 2001b, pp. 72–3)

Comment

In this example, Roz and her colleagues are clearly at a loss as to how to respond to the racist comments made by the white patient's wife about black patients. Roz herself acknowledges that – as a white person – she finds it very uncomfortable talking about racism, especially with black people.

Gunaratnam (the author of the research) recognises that talking about racism can be very threatening, especially as people may be scared about using the 'wrong' words, or saying something that is unintentionally offensive. A member of staff put it like this:

> I feel that the climate now, with equal opportunities and everything, that it is unacceptable at a professional level to be racist. So it is really difficult to be able to ask for help, it would be a bit like identifying yourself as having racist tendencies … To come forward … feels very frightening and daunting.

> (Quoted in Gunaratnam, 2001b, p. 79)

Although it can feel uncomfortable and threatening, Gunaratnam argues that it is important to talk honestly about dilemmas that arise in day-to-day practice, as this helps to create a more open climate. She also cautions that employers shouldn't take a rigid approach to dealing with racist incidents:

> … it is inappropriate to impose and also to expect staff to follow a single, 'correct' line of action [because] … different modes of intervention are required to address different … forms of racism.

> (Gunaratnam, 2001b, p. 81)

Instead, Gunaratnam advises that 'staff dilemmas' should be acknowledged, because this makes it easier to find solutions that are sensitive to particular situations. This is preferable to imposing a blanket 'politically correct' approach.

It is important that staff feel able to raise and discuss issues to do with racism in the workplace

In Rosie's case, no one talked about what was going on, so it would have been difficult for any individual to know what to do. In contrast, Roz found a way forward, not by consulting written guidelines but by talking about her uncertainty. From the outside, it might appear that Roz took no action – the black service users remained exposed to racist comments. In fact, she made a deliberate decision – in consultation with the black service users – to resist pressure to move the white patient into a room of his own. For as Roz pointed out, moving the patient would have sent out the message that she agreed with his wife's racist views.

The story of Roz's dilemma also makes the point that challenging racism doesn't have to involve a major confrontation. It can be just as effective for individual workers to question and talk about things they feel confused or uncomfortable about. But doing this can feel safe only in the right kind of organisational climate where workers feel they have the support of both colleagues and managers. Rosie had neither of these, and she felt powerless to argue.

3.3 Discrimination and power

Recognising the role of power relationships is central to understanding how racism and discrimination operate. Rosie felt powerless, and the same was likely to be true for most of her colleagues. As a course tester pointed out: 'The ward staff would probably have felt powerless to challenge the consultant paediatrician.' Think back to Unit 2, where hierarchies in hospital are discussed, and you will recognise that in traditional hospital settings, nurses seldom challenge doctors.

Power is a key ingredient in the process of discrimination. Look carefully at Figure 1, developed by Barn et al. (Organisational and Social Development Consultant, 1997), which explains how discrimination occurs.

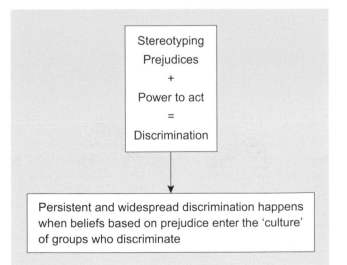

Figure 1 The process of discrimination (Source: adapted from OSDC, 1997)

Figure 1 suggests that discrimination arises out of a combination of factors. Rosie's case is a good example:

Prejudices. The white mother (by her own admission) held prejudiced beliefs about black people.

+ Power to act. Although the mother was not especially powerful as an individual, she was able to harness the power of the consultant and other senior hospital staff.

= Discrimination. The senior staff didn't intend to harm Rosie, but by using their power to accommodate prejudice instead of opposing it, they became complicit in the discrimination against Rosie.

Sometimes discrimination is about *not acting*. The employment tribunal ruled that the NHS Trust had wrongly complied with racist behaviour because they went along with the mother's wishes and did not intervene to stop the racism against Rosie. The Trust's actions were found to be racial discrimination under the Race Relations Act 1976.

3.4 The legal position

The Race Relations Act 1976 makes it unlawful for one person to discriminate on racial grounds against another. The Act defines racial grounds as including race, colour, nationality or ethnic or national origins. The law deals with racist actions, rather than with racist beliefs or intentions:

> It is not necessary to prove that the other person intended to discriminate against you: you only have to show that you received less favourable treatment as a result of what they did.

> (Equality and Human Rights Commission, 2007)

There is a legal difference, therefore, between *racism* (in the sense of a prejudiced belief) and *racial discrimination*. The consultant's actions may not have stemmed from racist beliefs, but nevertheless they resulted in racial discrimination. In this case, the consultant was not held individually responsible for what had happened: the tribunal's verdict was made against the organisation. Consequently, this is a case of institutional racism.

3.5 Institutional racism and institutional discrimination

The NHS Trust was found guilty of racial discrimination, even though there was no evidence that the individuals concerned held racist beliefs or intended any harm towards Rosie personally. Activity 9 suggests that the problem arose because:

- There was no organisational framework for acknowledging racism or discussing what had happened in terms of racism.

- The hospital didn't formally recognise racism; there was no policy setting out what action should be taken to address it.

Bhavnani et al. (2005, p. 150) argue that when people or organisations ignore racism, this is actually racism in another form. By acting as if racism were acceptable, and allowing it to continue, the NHS Trust was being 'institutionally racist'. The 1999 Macpherson Report, of the inquiry into the death of Stephen Lawrence, defined institutional racism as:

> The collective failure of an organisation to provide an appropriate and professional service to people because of their colour, culture, or ethnic origin. It can be seen or detected in processes, attitudes and behaviour

which amount to discrimination through unwitting prejudice, ignorance, thoughtlessness and racist stereotyping which disadvantage minority ethnic people.

(Macpherson, 1999, p. 28, para. 6.34)

The term 'institutional' can be used in connection with any kind of discrimination (such as institutional sexism or institutional ageism), but it is most often used in relation to racism. Institutional discrimination involves disadvantaging any group of people whose needs differ from the dominant group, and often occurs because the entire service is organised around the assumption that 'everyone is the same'. Here are some examples:

- A facility is 'open to everyone', but it is on the third floor and there is no lift. This means that people in wheelchairs cannot use the facility.

- A company insists that people cannot leave their desks during the day apart from toilet breaks and lunch. This means that practising Muslims cannot work there since they cannot pray at the appointed times.

(Forum on Discrimination, undated)

Sometimes, institutional discrimination occurs as a result of organisational systems. The Research on Age Discrimination Project (RoAD) found that older people are disadvantaged by the rules governing eligibility for various medical treatments. For instance, at the time of writing (in 2008), the NHS offers routine breast screening only to women aged between fifty and sixty-nine, even though women over the age of seventy continue to be at risk of breast cancer. This is just one example of institutional ageism in health and social care, but age is often used as the basis for categorising people and allocating funding and resources, which can have a negative impact on their access to specialist treatment or services (Bytheway et al., 2007, p. 46).

In this section, you have seen that racism goes beyond individual words and actions; it operates implicitly through the assumptions and processes embedded in organisations. This affects the organisational climate for both workers and service users. Racism is difficult to talk about in care work, but unless it is acknowledged, it can't be addressed. In the final section of this unit, you will read and hear about what health and social care organisations can do to create a more open and inclusive workplace, in order to respond to the needs of diverse communities.

Key points

- Racism involves both beliefs (prejudice) and ways of acting towards people (discrimination).

- Racism can be difficult to talk about in care work, but if staff feel unable to talk about it, they will not be able to challenge it when it is directed against service users.

- Written policies and a flexible, open organisational climate can make it easier for care workers to share their concerns and find solutions to racist behaviour.

- Institutional discrimination occurs when a service is organised around assumptions that disadvantage minority groups; this leads to a failure to acknowledge and challenge discrimination.

4 Positive responses to diversity in communities

The previous sections have looked at what individual workers can do to respond to people's diverse needs. The focus here will be mainly on the responsibilities of health and social care organisations more generally.

4.1 Making health and social care services more inclusive

Let's return to the example of short break services for black and minority ethnic disabled children. Flynn (2002) and other researchers have observed that there is a low take-up of short break (respite) care among black and minority ethnic families, despite evidence of a high demand. Two reasons were given for this:

- because these families lack information
- because the service isn't sensitive to the cultural needs of their children.

The next activity reviews the barriers that can prevent short break services from offering accessible care to black and minority ethnic disabled children, and looks at practical steps to overcome these.

Resources

Activity 11   What works in providing successful services for diverse communities?

Allow about 45 minutes

Return to Resource 13, 'Improving access to services for black and minority ethnic disabled children', by Shameem Nawaz. This time start at the beginning and read the whole article, leaving out the two sections headed 'Matching and linking' and 'Transracial placements', which you read for Activity 2.

Look at what Nawaz says about the barriers to providing a more inclusive service. Using the grid below, note down the author's suggestions for overcoming each of these. To help you, the barriers discussed by the author have been entered in the first column.

Barrier to providing a service to black and minority ethnic members of the community	How could this barrier be overcome?
Black and minority ethnic communities don't know what support is available	
Services are inappropriate to meet the cultural and religious needs of black and minority ethnic service users	
Workers lack the skills and experience to work with black and minority ethnic service users	
The particular skills of black and minority ethnic care workers are not utilised	

Comment

Compare your responses with the following.

Barrier to providing a service to black and minority ethnic members of the community	How could this barrier be overcome?
Black and minority ethnic communities don't know what support is available	Build a presence in local communities; engage in outreach and development work; provide information in appropriate formats; publicise by word of mouth
Services are inappropriate to meet the cultural and religious needs of black and minority ethnic service users	Have a diverse team of carers; recruit people who share the same culture as service users Managers need to take an active role so that they will commit the necessary resources – for training, interpreters, recruitment drives
Workers lack the skills and experience to work with black and minority ethnic service users	Recruit carers who speak the same languages as service users Support and provide training for staff (both white and black) about diversity
The particular skills of black and minority ethnic care workers are not utilised	Provide black and minority ethnic workers with opportunities for recognition and regular support

The solutions identified by Nawaz and her colleagues (in the right-hand column) provide a set of guidelines to help any service – not just short break care – to become more inclusive of black and minority ethnic communities. The barriers, and the guidelines for overcoming them, are also relevant to other groups of disadvantaged people. Let's look at some examples of how other agencies have sought to make their services more inclusive.

Engaging with local communities

Nawaz suggests that care services need to engage with local communities and neighbourhood organisations. One way of doing this is to develop an outreach approach, where agencies take the initiative in reaching out to people who might need their services. This can work better than expecting people from minority groups to come to an unfamiliar building. There were examples of outreach work in Unit 10: the Sussex Traveller Women's Health project, and the family support projects in Thornhill and Tower Hamlets. All are ways of taking services out to where people live. You will also remember the Thornhill Community Access Project, which helped isolated and excluded people to make contact with other agencies.

TravellerSpace

St.Day Gypsy and Traveller Women's Group meets once a week during term time at the St.Day Children's Centre. It is attended by Gypsy, Irish Traveller and New Traveller women and their pre-school children.

We set the group up in partnership with the health visitor for the near by site in October 2005.

There's not room to list all the activities that take place at this busy group, but they include: a mother and toddler group, craft activities, healthy cooking, sewing, first aid training, drug and alcohol awareness training, access to the internet, film making and tea drinking.

Other agencies have found the group a useful way of engaging with Gypsies and Travellers and it is regularly attended by Family Learning who provide literacy support, Cornwall Adult Social Care who can help with form filling, making appointments, benefits advice and any other problems that may come up, the Dental Service and the Stop Smoking Service and the health visitor.

Engaging with local communities: TravellerSpace is an independent voluntary organisation supporting Gypsies and Travellers in Cornwall. It works with statutory agencies to take services out to the places where Travellers live

Having a diverse staff team

Nawaz highlights the importance of recruiting a diverse staff team which can respond to different needs in the local community, and this was also a feature of the projects referred to above. Employing staff from minority groups is not sufficient in itself, however. Nawaz underlines the importance of providing training and support with diversity issues for all staff. Although there are clear advantages in matching staff and service users who share the same culture and language, this shouldn't mean that white staff never work with black service users (or vice versa). The most important thing is to meet the particular needs of service users, by utilising all workers' skills and experiences to best advantage.

Some organisations find it a particular advantage to employ people who have had similar experiences to service users. For example, in Nottinghamshire, ex-drug and alcohol users are employed in substance misuse services. Their past experience, skills and knowledge are thus channelled back into the substance misuse workforce, for the benefit of current service users. At Breakthrough UK, a Manchester organisation which supports disabled people to gain employment, over 60% of employees are disabled themselves (Breakthrough, undated).

The commitment of managers

Although the skills of frontline care workers are vital in engaging with service users at face-to-face level, an inclusive service also relies on the commitment of managers. Senior staff usually have at least some influence over the use of resources, and are responsible for recruiting and training staff. They have to ensure that anti-discriminatory legislation is complied with, and – equally important – they are responsible for setting the organisational climate.

In the second half of this section you will hear the manager and staff of the Somebody Cares home care agency explaining how they deal with diversity issues for staff and service users.

4.2 A real-life example

The Somebody Cares home care agency, which you first encountered in Unit 3, is located in Cardiff, which has the most ethnically diverse population in Wales:

> Nearly 12% of its population of just over 300,000 are from ethnic groups other than White British, according to the 2001 Census.
>
> The largest minority group is Asian, which makes up nearly 4% of the city's population, or more than 12,000 people.
>
> [...]
>
> Cardiff has nearly 4,000 black residents ... The majority of these (almost two-thirds) are of Somali descent. There have been two distinct phases in the history of Somalis in Cardiff. The first was in the late nineteenth century, when sailors from the then British protectorate of Somaliland served in Britain's royal and merchant navies ... The second phase came with the arrival of refugees from the war-torn country during the 1980s and 1990s. This latter group now forms the majority of the Somali population in Cardiff.
>
> In recent years, Cardiff has also seen a sharp rise in the number of Bangladeshi residents ...
>
> Cardiff also has an unusually high proportion of residents of Mixed ethnic origin. More than 6,000 people (2% of all people) described themselves in this way in the 2001 census. The largest sub-group within this category was White and Black Caribbean, at nearly 2,500.

(Commission for Racial Equality, 2007)

Another feature of Cardiff is that over 16% of people can read, write or understand the Welsh language. Almost 11% of these are fluent Welsh speakers. Under the Welsh Language Act (implemented in 1993), public services have to use both English and Welsh in conducting their business (Cardiff Council, undated).

In the next activity, you will hear Julie Borek, Managing Director of Somebody Cares, explaining how the agency goes about recruiting and supporting a diverse staff team, and how it responds to service users' needs. You will also hear three members of the staff team talking from a 'ground level' perspective.

DVD

Activity 12   Responding to diversity at the Somebody Cares agency

Allow about 20 minutes

Find Block 3, Unit 11, Activity 12 on the DVD. Listen to Julie Borek and staff from the Somebody Cares agency talking about diversity, and follow the instructions given.

Comment

The Somebody Cares agency provides a good example of the practical steps that can be taken to meet the needs of a diverse community. Julie Borek, the Managing Director, is keen to recruit care staff with varied backgrounds, and she supports them if they have particular needs. There is also a written equal opportunities policy.

Julie Borek, Managing Director of the Somebody Cares agency

Equal opportunities policies, according to Gunaratnam (2000), make it easier for staff and managers to talk about racism and deal with it. At Somebody Cares, however, the policy is not just a paper exercise. One of the agency's key strengths is that the Director is committed to maintaining a high quality of provision for all service users. In order to achieve this, she recognises the importance of creating a safe and positive organisational climate for staff. If Rosie Purves had worked here, she might still have experienced racism, but it would have been faced openly and dealt with, and she would have felt valued and supported.

Gunaratnam argues that employers should take a flexible approach to dealing with diversity issues, rather than adhering rigidly to a particular approach. At Somebody Cares, this is illustrated by the dilemma that occurred when staff needed to (a) remove their shoes to show respect for a service user's culture, and (b) comply with health and safety regulations. After careful thought and discussion with the service user, an acceptable and practical compromise was found: the agency bought some plastic covers for care workers to wear over their own footwear.

Elvis Malcolm, home care worker at Somebody Cares, feels confident that he will be listened to and supported if he experiences racism at work

4.3 Anti-discriminatory legislation

At the start of this unit, you read that health and social care services often take a 'diversity approach' which values people's differences. As Thompson (2006, p. 11) outlines, the diversity approach includes making a commitment to address all forms of unfair discrimination. Since around the turn of the century, a raft of new anti-discriminatory legislation has been introduced, for example: the Race Relations (Amendment) Act 2000; employment regulations governing discrimination on the grounds of sexual orientation and religion (implemented in 2003) and on the grounds of age (implemented in 2006); and the Disability Discrimination Acts 1995 and 2005. While legislation has its limits (Thompson, 2006) – for example, it may not cover all forms of discrimination, and some people may not disclose their concerns and experiences – it forms a framework for protecting service users and care workers from discrimination.

In the next activity, you will be able to examine one example of this legislation: the law relating to racial discrimination. To make this come to life, you are going to find out how this legislation applies to a real organisation, using the example of the Somebody Cares agency.

Activity 13   Race relations legislation

Allow about 30 minutes

IVR   DVD

Log on to the course website and click on the link to the HSC Resource Bank. Then click on 'Law' from the range of options presented. As the Somebody Cares agency is located in Cardiff, you will need to look for the set of resources that relates to Wales. Among the resources on discrimination, you will find a summary of the law relating to racial discrimination. The law resources are updated on a regular basis, but at the time of writing (in 2008) the relevant legislation is the Race Relations Act 1976 and recent amendments.

(a) Note down two examples of what the Somebody Cares agency's main responsibilities are (as a public body), under this legislation.

(b) Now jot down what you think service users and staff could do if they had a complaint under the legislation.

Comment

(a) You will see that the agency has a number of duties to combat unlawful racial discrimination, and to promote equality of opportunity and good relationships between people from different ethnic groups. At the time of writing, these include a duty for public bodies to ensure that minority ethnic groups have access to information about, and can access, the service. Another duty is to avoid discrimination against staff; for example, in relation to selection processes and training opportunities.

(b) It is clear from Activity 12 that Julie Borek, the Managing Director, would encourage both staff and service users to contact her and let her know if they had any complaints. Indeed, Elvis Malcolm seemed confident that Julie would respond effectively to any such issues. Most care organisations provide contact details so service users and staff can express their concerns to a manager in the first instance. However, as you might have suggested, people could also seek free legal advice; for example, from a Citizens' Advice Bureau, or from the internet (the Commission for Equality and Human Rights website, www.equalityhumanrights.com, for instance). Staff could get advice from a trade union such as Unison.

The race relations laws are just one aspect of anti-discriminatory legislation, and if you are interested in finding out about the other kinds, you will find more information in the HSC Resource Bank.

Learning skills: Using the HSC Resource Bank

Activity 13 has introduced you to the HSC Resource Bank. There will be further opportunities to use the HSC Resource Bank in Unit 12. You don't need to wait until then, however. It's a good idea to access the HSC Resource Bank from time to time and browse around. There is a lot of information you could find very useful, either for your everyday life or for your essays.

As you saw in Activity 13, public bodies have particular duties under the race discrimination laws. Similar legal obligations – 'equality duties' – exist in relation to disability equality and gender equality, and apply to a range of public organisations, including local authorities, the NHS, educational establishments, and private sector organisations that deliver services under contract to public bodies. The equality duties extend and add a new emphasis to previous legislation. To illustrate the way in which the equality duties work, imagine that a supported living service for people with learning disabilities finds that it has very few black and minority ethnic service users. One of the disability equality duties is to 'promote equality of opportunity between disabled persons and other persons' (Disability Rights Commission, 2005, p. 13). To comply with this duty (and improve its service), the organisation might decide to employ outreach workers to make contact with black and minority ethnic communities and consult them about how the service could be developed to meet their needs (DRC, 2005, p. 15). In other words, public bodies now have to take steps to *promote* equality, rather than just respond to individual complaints about shortfalls.

This final section of Unit 11 has considered ways in which health and social care agencies can make their services more sensitive and responsive to the diverse needs of the communities they serve. Summarising these, you have seen that:

- Agencies need to engage with local communities to find out about their needs and to make sure that they are aware of what the agency provides.

- Managers need to take steps to ensure that the workforce reflects the diversity of the local community.

- Managers play a key role in setting an open and inclusive organisational climate.

- Anti-discriminatory legislation and equal opportunities policies provide a useful framework for good practice.

Before ending your work on this unit, give some thought to the nurse who eventually felt able to speak out on Rosie Purves' behalf. Rosie explains in Chapter 3 of the Reader:

> One brave nurse who attended the tribunal gave a statement on my behalf. … She said that she was asked one day to move a child and when asked why, was told, 'Because mum doesn't want Rosie or any black person to look after their child.' She said she realised she should have challenged this but didn't.

(Reader, Chapter 3, p. 24)

If the organisation had taken the diversity approach you have been reading about, perhaps Rosie's colleague would have said something sooner. At least she would have felt able to talk about and question what was happening. On this occasion, a care worker experienced discrimination. Next time, it could be a service user.

Key points

- By engaging with their local communities, care agencies can find out about diverse needs and use this information to develop appropriate services.

- Having a diverse staff team helps care services to respond to different needs in the local community; however, all staff have a role to play in working with minority communities (of all kinds).

- Managers play a key role in the quality and direction of the service, and are responsible for setting the organisational climate.

- Anti-discriminatory legislation and workplace policies form a framework for protecting service users and care workers from discrimination.

Conclusion

In Unit 11 you have explored a variety of concepts relating to diversity and its implications for health and social care. You saw that diversity itself is a complex idea, involving not just a recognition of people's differences, but an understanding that difference can lead to negative judgements being made about some groups of people. You looked at examples of stereotyping and prejudices, and saw how important it is for care workers to avoid using these as the basis for providing a service. You explored some real-life experiences of racism against health workers and service users, and saw that dealing effectively with it requires care workers to be able to talk about difficult issues. Finally, you looked at some positive examples of what health and social care organisations can do to meet the challenge of diversity in communities.

Learning skills: Taking control of your time

In Unit 10, you thought about the little unnecessary distractions which so easily undermine your concentration as you study. But not all distractions are trivial – pressures at work, the needs of children, worries about untouched housework, getting the toilet repaired. Are you feeling doubly guilty right now – first, about what you have fallen short of achieving *in* your studies, and second, about what you have fallen short of achieving *because of* your studies? Is this whole study thing a bad idea?

How can you balance all the demands from outside K101 with your own need for personal development through study? What are the priorities in your life? The fact is that some things just won't get done – or won't get done as thoroughly as before you were studying. But are you giving more time to K101 than you can really afford? Or are there other things you need to drop, to take some of the pressure off? Do you need to talk to people in your life to explain the demands on your time?

Now that you have some experience of K101, you need to be looking for a balance in your life as an independent student. You need to weigh up what is important so that you can 'grant yourself' a suitable amount of study time. You get the worst of all worlds if you find yourself wasting hard-won study time worrying about what you are not doing elsewhere.

> I've restructured my time to ensure I'm not rushing around at the last minute to get things finished, and I'm making sure now that I work in a room alone without any interruptions!! Just means my husband will have grey hair and a headache before me – looking after the kids!! What a shame eh?

Reader

Taking control of how you use your time is a key part of being successful as a student. Read about the cases of Ryan and Tracy in Section 2.1 of *The Good Study Guide*, and then, in Section 2.2, about some techniques you can try using to manage your studies (pages 26–33).

End-of-unit checklist

Studying this unit should have helped you to:

- discuss the concept of diversity in relation to communities, and some challenges for care agencies in responding to it
- explain what stereotyping, prejudice and discrimination mean, and discuss their implications for people's experiences of accessing health and social care services in the community
- recognise the importance of acknowledging racism in care settings, and understand what managers can do to encourage care workers to be open about their concerns
- give an account of what health and social care organisations can do to respond positively to diversity in communities, in relation to both service users and care workers.

References

BBC (undated) *Romany Roots: Amy* [online], www.bbc.co.uk/kent/voices/amy.shtml (Accessed 13 March 2008).

BBC News (2004) *Black Care Ban Nurse Wins Payout*, 17 May [online], news.bbc.co.uk/1/hi/england/hampshire/dorset/3721995.stm (Accessed 13 March 2008).

Bhavnani, R., Mirza, H. and Meetoo, V. (2005) *Tackling the Roots of Racism*, Bristol, The Policy Press.

Bignall, T. and Box, L. (2002) *Engaging Black and Minority Ethnic Families in Policy Development and Implementation*, Black and Minority Ethnic Families Policy Forum, Discussion Paper No. 6, London, Race Equality Unit [online], www.reu.org.uk/projects/files/paper6_engagingfamilies.pdf (Accessed 13 March 2008).

Bolton at Home (undated) *Valuing Diversity Strategy: Summary 2005–2008* [online], www.boltonathome.org.uk/content/Valuing%20Diversity%20Strategy%20Summary %20Document.doc (Accessed 13 March 2008).

Breakthrough (undated) *Breakthrough Wins Positive Action Award* [online], www.breakthrough-uk.com/index.shtml (Accessed 13 March 2008).

Bristol City Council (2006) *Gypsies and Travellers: Frequently Asked Questions – Myths and the Facts* [online], www.bristol.gov.uk/ccm/cms-service/stream/asset/ ;jsessionid=E577F728C08A0687112EE1128E7C9AFC?asset_id=10845088& (Accessed 13 March 2008).

Butt, J. (2006) *Are We There Yet? Identifying the Characteristics of Social Care Organisations that Successfully Promote Diversity*, Stakeholder Participation Race Equality Discussion Paper 3, London, Social Care Institute for Excellence [online], www.scie.org.uk/publications/raceequalitydiscussionpapers/redp03.pdf (Accessed 13 March 2008).

Bytheway, B., Ward, R., Holland, C. and Peace, S. (2007) *Too Old: Older People's Accounts of Discrimination, Exclusion and Rejection; A Report from the Research on Age Discrimination Project (RoAD) to Help the Aged*, London, Help the Aged.

Cardiff Council (undated) *The Welsh Language Scheme* [online], www.cardiff.gov.uk/ content.asp?Parent_Directory_id=2865&nav=2872,3259,5018 (Accessed 13 March 2008).

Chamba, R., Ahmad, W., Hirst, M., Lawton, D. and Beresford, B. (1999) *On the Edge: Minority Ethnic Families Caring for a Severely Disabled Child*, Bristol, The Policy Press.

Chambers, C. and Alexis, O. (2004) 'Creating an inclusive environment for black and minority ethnic nurses', *British Journal of Nursing*, vol. 13, no. 22, pp. 1355–8.

Commission for Racial Equality (2007) *Ethnicity Profiles: Wales – Cardiff* [online], http://83.137.212.42/sitearchive/cre/diversity/map/wales/cardiff.html (Accessed 13 March 2008).

Disability Rights Commission (DRC) (2005) *The Social Care Sector and the Disability Equality Duty: A Guide to the Disability Equality Duty and Disability Discrimination Act 2005 for Social Care Organisations* [online], www.equalityhumanrights.com/ Documents/DRC/Useful%20Documents/The%20Social%20Care%20sector%20and %20the%20Disability%20Equality%20Duty.pdf (Accessed 17 March 2008).

Equality and Human Rights Commission (2007) *What is Race Discrimination?* [online], www.equalityhumanrights.com/en/yourrights/equalityanddiscrimination/race/Pages/ Whatisracediscimination.aspx (Accessed 13 March 2008).

Fazil, Q., Bywaters, P., Ali, Z., Wallace, L. and Singh, G. (2002) 'Disadvantage and discrimination compounded: the experience of Pakistani and Bangladeshi parents of disabled children in the UK', *Disability and Society*, vol. 17, no. 3, pp. 237–53.

Flynn, R. (2002) *Short Breaks: Providing Better Access and More Choice for Black Disabled Children and their Parents*, Bristol, The Policy Press.

Forum on Discrimination (undated) *What is Discrimination?* [online], www.forumondiscrimination.org.uk/fond/fond_display.jsp?pContentID=635&p_applic=CCC&p_service=Content.show& (Accessed 13 March 2008).

Gilchrist, A. (2004) *The Well Connected Community: A Networking Approach to Community Development*, Bristol, The Policy Press.

Gunaratnam, Y. (2000) 'Implications of the Stephen Lawrence Inquiry for palliative care', *International Journal of Palliative Nursing*, vol. 6, no. 3, pp. 147–9.

Gunaratnam, Y. (2001a) 'Eating into multiculturalism: hospice staff and service users talk food, "race", ethnicity, culture and identity', *Critical Social Policy*, vol. 21, no. 3, pp. 287–310.

Gunaratnam, Y. (2001b) '"We mustn't judge people … but": staff dilemmas in dealing with racial harassment amongst hospice service users', *Sociology of Health and Illness*, vol. 23, no. 1, pp. 65–84.

Haynes, J., Tikly, L. and Caballero, C. (2006) 'The barriers to achievement for White/Black Caribbean pupils in English schools', *British Journal of Sociology of Education*, vol. 27, no. 5, pp. 569–83.

Independent Schools Council (undated) *Adapting to British Culture* [online], www.isc.co.uk/InternationalZone_AdaptingtoBritishCulture.htm (Accessed 13 March 2008).

Macpherson, W. (1999) *The Stephen Lawrence Inquiry: Report of an Inquiry by Sir William Macpherson of Cluny*, London, The Stationery Office; also available online at www.archive.official-documents.co.uk/document/cm42/4262/4262.htm (Accessed 13 March 2008).

Mind (2007) *New Research Reveals Alarming Increase in Mental Health Prejudice in England,* Press Release, 6 July [online], www.mind.org.uk/News+policy+and+campaigns/Press/AW2007-07-06publicattitudes.htm (Accessed 13 March 2008).

Molloy, D., Knight, T. and Woodfield, K. (2003) *Diversity in Disability: Exploring the Interactions between Disability, Ethnicity, Age, Gender and Sexuality*, Research Report No. 188, Leeds, Department for Work and Pensions [online], www.dwp.gov.uk/asd/asd5/rports2003-2004/rrep188.asp (Accessed 13 March 2008).

Organisational and Social Development Consultant (OSDC) (1997) *Understanding Racism and Developing Good Practice*, Basingstoke, Macmillan.

Owens, A. and Randhawa, G. (2004) '"It's different from my culture; they're very different": providing community-based, "culturally competent" palliative care for South Asian people in the UK', *Health and Social Care in the Community*, vol. 12, no. 5, pp. 414–21.

Press Association (2004) 'Nurse wins £20,000 in race case', *Guardian*, 18 May [online], www.guardian.co.uk/race/story/0,,1219135,00.html (Accessed 13 March 2008).

Price, E. (2005) 'All but invisible: older gay men and lesbians', *Nursing Older People*, vol. 17, no. 4, pp. 16–18.

renewal.net (undated) *Project Recruit* (Case Study) [online], www.renewal.net/Documents/RNET/Case%20Study/Projectrecruit.doc (Accessed 13 March 2008).

Royal College of Nursing and UNISON (undated) *Not 'Just' a Friend: Best Practice Guidance on Health Care for Lesbian, Gay and Bisexual Service Users and Their Families* [online], www.unison.org.uk/file/B1287.doc (Accessed 13 March 2008).

Sapey, B., Stewart, J. and Donaldson, G. (2005) 'Increases in wheelchair use and perceptions of disablement', *Disability and Society*, vol. 20, no. 5, pp. 489–505.

Scottish Government (2003) *Improving the Health of the Scottish Minority Ethnic Communities: Annual Report of the Steering Committee and the Director of the National Resource Centre for Ethnic Minority Health 2002–2003. Appendix E Glossary of Terms Used in the National Assessment Framework* [online], www.scotland.gov.uk/Publications/2003/11/18478/28754 (Accessed 13 March 2008).

Shah, R. (1995) *The Silent Minority: Children with Disabilities in Asian Families*, London, National Children's Bureau.

Stonewall (undated) *Profiles of Prejudice: Detailed Summary of Findings* [online], www.stonewallscotland.org.uk/documents/long_summary_no_logo.doc (Accessed 13 March 2008).

Sutherland, A. (2006) *The Other Tradition: From Personal Politics to Disability Arts*, Disability Studies Association Conference, Lancaster University, 19 September [online], www.disabilitystudies.net/index.php?content=23& action=2006; also available at www.leeds.ac.uk/disability-studies/archiveuk/Sutherland/The%20Other%20Tradition.pdf (Both accessed 13 March 2008).

Tarleton, B. and Macaulay, F. (2002) *Better for the Break? Short Break Services for Children and Teenagers with Autistic Spectrum Disorders and their Families*, Barnardo's [online], www.bristol.ac.uk/norahfry/download/betterfindings.pdf (Accessed 13 March 2008).

Thompson, N. (2006) *Anti-discriminatory Practice* (4th edn), Basingstoke, Palgrave Macmillan.

TNS for Shift, CSIP (2007) *Attitudes to Mental Illness 2007*, Department of Health [online], www.dh.gov.uk/en/Publicationsandstatistics/Publications/PublicationsStatistics/DH_076516 (Accessed 13 March 2008).

Valentine, G. and McDonald, I. (2004) *Understanding Prejudice: Attitudes Towards Minorities*, Stonewall [online], www.stonewallscotland.org.uk/information_bank/research/default.asp#Understanding_Prejudice (Accessed 13 March 2008).

Van Cleemput, P., Thomas, K., Parry, G., Peters, J., Moore, J. and Cooper, C. (2004) *The Health Status of Gypsies and Travellers in England: Report of Qualitative Findings*, University of Sheffield, School of Health and Related Research [online], www.shef.ac.uk/scharr/research/publications/travellers.html (Accessed 13 March 2008).

Willmott, P. (1989) *Community Initiatives: Patterns and Prospects*, London, Policy Studies Institute.

Website

www.equalityhumanrights.com (Accessed 21 June 2008).

Unit 12

Supporting people to use community resources

Prepared for the course team by Fran Wiles

Contents

Introduction

In this final week of Block 3, the focus changes once again to 'skills'. As usual, Section 1 focuses on care skills, specifically the skills involved in helping people to use community resources. You begin with some reading to provide a context for the skills activities, but most of the care skills activities are on the DVD. Section 2 carries on the work you have been doing in developing number skills, this time following up the discussion in Unit 9 with more figures on poverty in the UK. And Section 3 explores more of the learning skills that will help you to succeed with K101. The unit will take about six hours to complete, leaving you time to work on the next assignment.

Are you taking the IVR?

If you are studying K101 as part of the Integrated Vocational Route (IVR), don't forget to check your VQ Candidate Handbook to see which Unit 12 activities contribute to your electronic portfolio.

1 Care skills: supporting people to use community resources

In Block 3, you have been exploring the relationship between health and social care services and the communities they serve. In Unit 9, you looked at how community-based services and facilities can have benefits for health and well-being; in Units 10 and 11 you encountered some of the difficulties people have in getting access to services provided in the community. In this unit, the focus is on developing your own skills in working in the community. It may be that you have a lot of experience of working in community settings, either as a paid worker or as a volunteer. Perhaps the kind of community-based health and social care services described in Units 9 to 11 were familiar to you from your own experience. If this is the case, this unit will give you an opportunity to reflect on some of the skills that you have gained through this work, and to practise them further. Or perhaps you are involved in care work, but not in a community setting. If so, this unit may help you to develop skills that will be useful in the future. Finally, you may not be directly involved in any form of care work, whether paid or unpaid. However, working through the activities in this unit will help to consolidate what you have learned in Units 9 to 11, by giving you the chance to apply it to some practical examples.

1.1 What's involved in supporting people to use community resources?

The particular skill on which this unit focuses is *supporting people to use community resources*. This involves:

- helping someone to identify and communicate what they want to do and achieve

- supporting them in finding suitable services and facilities

- taking account of the practical and personal issues which may arise

- making sure the agreed arrangements are put in place.

Throughout Units 9, 10 and 11, you have seen examples of people using services and facilities in the community. These have ranged from visiting a GP or attending a community midwives' session, to taking part in neighbourhood activities such as t'ai chi and the 'Cooking Pots' group organised by the Thornhill Health and Wellbeing Project. As you have seen, some people need assistance to access these facilities. For example, Nadia helped Mina to see her GP, and afterwards to attend her hospital appointments. She also helped Mina to contact a support group for people with the same health condition. The Community Access Project in Thornhill, and the Age Concern projects you read about in Resource 8 (by Eileen McLeod and colleagues), are further examples of paid and voluntary workers supporting people to make contact with local services and community facilities.

Care workers in a variety of roles and settings can be involved in supporting people to use community resources. Some care workers may be employed entirely for this purpose: this was the case with the Age Concern social rehabilitation (SR) workers. While I was writing this unit, a quick search on the internet revealed that many organisations employ 'community support workers'.

An agency which provides services for people with mental health problems explained on its website that: 'your Community-support Worker will visit you at the agreed times and offer you the support that has been agreed – whether that involves going with you to the shops or supporting you to sort out bills' (Together, 2008). Often, however, this kind of work forms part of a care worker's broader role; for example, a residential support worker might help a service user to access community facilities. My internet search found community support staff who work with people who have brain injuries acquired as a result of accident or illness. These workers provide support with people's physical needs as well as with their social, leisure and vocational needs (Brain Injury Rehabilitation Trust, undated).

1.2 An example

To explore the skills involved in this work, let's take an example from Resource 8.

Do you remember the man who was supported to take up fishing again? This was especially important to him, not only because it was a hobby he enjoyed, but also because it was how he maintained contact with his friends. Read this short extract as a reminder:

[*Social rehabilitation worker]

An SR worker[*] enabled a service user to access his favourite former hobby – fishing, despite the onset of long term physical impairments. The service user could no longer drive to the fishing plots or cast his line. Using her advocacy skills, the SR worker contacted some fishing clubs and found people willing to drive the service user regularly to fish, bait his line and give other help where needed. The service user's physical health and stamina were recorded as improved, as was his emotional well-being on being able to resume a former activity and social life that had previously seemed permanently closed to him …

To make the discussion easier, I'll call the service user Peter Jones. Let's say he's a man in his early seventies who lives alone and uses a wheelchair after partially recovering from a stroke. I'll call the worker Helen Davies. There were several stages that Helen and Peter had to go through before Peter could start fishing again:

- Firstly, Helen had to talk with Peter about the changes he wanted to make in order to resume his way of life, now that he had come out of hospital. She needed to find out about Peter's interests and how his health condition affected his daily living.

- Once she had understood how much Peter wanted to go fishing again, Helen had to set about finding a suitable club. She used advocacy skills to help Peter express his needs and to act on his behalf. She explained Peter's needs to club organisers and explored what kind of help the club could offer. She then had to discuss the options with Peter so that he could decide what he wanted to do.

- Once Peter had decided which club to join, Helen had to help him consider the practical arrangements. There would have been membership forms to fill in, and fees to pay. There was the issue of transport to arrange with the club.

One of the club members had volunteered to assist, and Helen supported Peter to explain clearly what he needed. For example, in addition to help with baiting his fishing line, Peter might need assistance in getting to the toilet. Helen could also help Peter to find out if any specialised equipment was available. She discussed possible risks with Peter and the club organiser, and clarified whether any special arrangements were needed to keep Peter safe. Because Peter lives by himself, the only other person to take into account was the home care worker who needed to know that Peter would be out for the day. However, if Peter had lived with an informal carer, Helen would have needed to take their perspective into account. For example, a carer's cooperation would be needed to help Peter get ready to leave the house earlier than usual.

- Finally, Helen had to make sure that all the arrangements had been set up, and be prepared to make changes if things didn't go as planned.

1.3 Drawing on previous learning

Although the focus in this unit is on *skills*, the reading you have done in Block 3 is also important to consider because it informs and enhances a care worker's skills. For example, Helen needed knowledge about what helps people to enjoy good health and well-being. The skills you have practised in earlier blocks are also relevant here. Helen needed to use good communication skills (Unit 8). The principles of care practice (Unit 4) would also have guided Helen's practice.

Knowledge about health and well-being

Think back to Labonte's model of health and well-being (Unit 9, Section 1.1, Figure 1), which shows the interrelationships between the physical, mental and social dimensions of well-being. The model placed much significance on the role of social relationships in maintaining good health.

You will know from Resource 8 that the Age Concern project was set up to help people resume and develop their social networks when their lives had been disrupted by illness. It's probable that some of Peter's social networks will have fallen away since his stroke, and as you will know, this is likely to have adverse effects on his well-being. It also limits the potential support available to him.

Using Labonte's model, it can be seen that resuming his hobby will have many benefits for Peter's well-being:

- Peter's physical well-being will be enhanced by the gentle exercise involved in getting out of the house and off to the fishing venue, as well as by the activity of fishing itself.

- His mental well-being will be improved by being able to do something he enjoys and which holds purpose for him.

- Feeling part of the fishing community and meeting new (and perhaps old) friends will be good for Peter's social well-being.

Looking at the interrelationships between the different kinds of well-being, you can see that in addition to the health benefits, being able to resume his former hobby will help Peter to feel more connected to his community and more in control of his life.

Communication skills

In Unit 8 you considered a variety of communication skills which care workers use when supporting people. You may wish to remind yourself of these by looking back at your previous work. In Peter's case, it's possible that Helen needed to take account of hearing loss or speech difficulties, which can follow a stroke. Even if this is not the case, Helen would have needed to listen carefully and empathically to what Peter was saying. Talking about his former life might have raised difficult emotions for Peter. He probably wouldn't have found it easy to talk about his personal needs. Differences in age and gender may have come into play here too.

In Unit 10 you saw that some people need an independent advocate to help them communicate their wishes. This might be the case if the usual worker is unfamiliar with the person's language or method of communication. For example, you read about a bilingual health advocacy scheme which was set up to support hospital patients who don't speak English as their first language.

An advocate might also be needed when someone is at risk of not being heard, or when there are conflicting interests. Do you remember Simon, who is isolated and vulnerable? Imagine that you are a social worker or community nurse who has become involved with Simon. Conditions in his flat have deteriorated even further, and the housing officer says that Simon will have to move into alternative accommodation while major repairs are carried out. Simon refuses to budge. You feel pulled in two directions. You want to help Simon, and you don't think he is coping on his own. This would be a good opportunity for him to move into supported accommodation where there are staff to assist him. But you can also see that Simon is strongly opposed to this. In addition, your organisation works very closely with the housing office, and you feel unable to represent Simon's interests impartially. In the circumstances, you might decide that Simon's needs would be best served by an independent advocate.

Principles of care practice

Underpinning everything that Helen did are the principles of care practice which guided her work. All five of the K101 *principles of care practice* (which you first read about in Unit 4) are applicable to the skill of helping people to use community resources. In particular, the following three are relevant here:

- Support people in maximising their potential
- Support people in having a voice and being heard
- Support people's rights to appropriate services.

Let's explore how these relate to Helen's work with Peter.

Support people in maximising their potential

Helen needed to develop a care relationship with Peter, in which she provided 'active support' which would encourage him to do as much as possible for himself. It was important that she didn't try to make all the decisions and arrangements for him. By taking the time to find out what Peter wanted to do, Helen was able to help him resume his former hobby to the best of his abilities. The way in which she did this also helped Peter to maintain independence and control over his life.

Support people in having a voice and being heard

Helen supported Peter in expressing his views and preferences. She didn't try to impose her own idea of 'what's best', but kept him at the centre of what she was doing. She took the time to listen to Peter, and tried to find information that would meet his needs. She shared this with Peter so that the decision remained within his control.

Support people's rights to appropriate services

Having found out about Peter's needs and wishes, Helen explored different options to meet these. She worked with Peter and the club organiser to make sure that Peter would get the level of support he required. Helen also took a creative approach to Peter's health and well-being needs. The fishing club isn't part of a mainstream service, but is something that can be provided in the general community.

So, to sum up, the skill of supporting people to use community resources involves:

- helping someone to identify and communicate what they want to do and achieve

- supporting them in finding suitable services and facilities

- taking account of the practical and personal issues which may arise

- making sure that the agreed arrangements are put in place.

Now you will get a chance to see these skills in action and try them out in some related activities on the DVD.

DVD

Activity 1   Supporting people to use community resources
Allow about an hour and a half

The rest of your work for this care skills element of Unit 12 is on the DVD. In the activities, you will see Sanjay Persaud, a community support worker, helping a young man called Ben Williams to find local activities to meet his interests.

Find Block 3, Unit 12, Activity 1 on the DVD.

Comment

Through observing and analysing the care relationship between Sanjay and Ben, you have developed your skills in helping people to use facilities in the community. This has included:

- using good communication to help someone express their needs

- researching a range of options to find suitable resources

- taking account of practical and other issues

- putting arrangements in place to enable the plan to happen

- working in partnership with service users, and in consultation with carers and other key people.

These skills will be particularly important if you are registered for the K101 Integrated Vocational Route (IVR).

Key points

- Helping people to use facilities in the community involves a range of skills: listening and communicating; researching options; taking account of practical issues; and putting arrangements in place.

- This needs to be done in partnership with service users, and in consultation with carers and other key people.

- The principles of care practice can be used as a resource to guide care workers in supporting people to use community facilities.

2 Working with numbers

As in Units 4 and 8, you now have an activity to develop your skills in making sense of tables and charts. In this unit, you will be following up the Unit 9 discussion of statistics showing the way in which levels of health and well-being in Scottish communities tend to reflect income levels. You will be looking at figures taken from an annually produced report: *Monitoring Poverty and Social Exclusion* (Palmer et al., 2007).

DVD

Activity 2   How much poverty is there in the UK today?

Allow about 30 minutes

To explore this question, find Block 3, Unit 12, Activity 2 on the DVD.

Before returning here, it will be a good idea to complete the iCMA.

Comment

As you keep working on these number skills activities, you should find that you are building up a more detailed picture of UK society and of the nature of the need for care services.

3 Learning skills

The learning skills section has three parts this time.

- First, you explore the Health and Social Care Resource Bank – a valuable resource available to all students of Open University courses in health and social care.

- Then, because you are about halfway through the course, there are some exercises to help you look back over what you have achieved so far, followed by exercises which look forward to what lies ahead.

- Finally, you explore another aspect of writing skills.

3.1 Using the Health and Social Care Resource Bank

How accurate and up to date is your knowledge of health and social care services in the UK, and of the government departments, laws, budgets, regulations, authorities and organisations by means of which they are delivered? Not only are the systems and structures for delivering care in the UK complex, they vary across the nations and are in constant flux, so keeping abreast is a daunting task. To help you out, the OU's Faculty of Health and Social Care maintains an online resource bank (the HSC-RB), which offers a digest of key information, presented in an accessible form. The HSC-RB is designed to let you select how much information you want to see and whether to view it for the whole of the UK, or just for your own nation within the UK. The next activity will help you to explore it and to think about how you might make use of it.

DVD

Activity 3   Exploring the HSC Resource Bank

Allow about 20 minutes

For this activity, go to Block 3, Unit 12, Activity 3 on the DVD.

Comment

You can find out a lot by using the HSC-RB. The main sections relevant to K101 are:

- **'Milestones'**: a timeline of key events in the development of health and social care in the UK, which you can use flexibly to highlight what you want to explore

- **'Care systems and structures'**: a set of brief outlines of how care services are organised in England, Northern Ireland, the Republic of Ireland, Scotland and Wales

- **'Law'**: a set of summaries of aspects of law which apply to health and social care in England, Northern Ireland, Scotland and Wales.

The purpose of this short activity has been to make you aware of the availability of the resource bank, and to take you through the basics of looking things up. If you want to make more extensive explorations, you can use the guidance provided within the resource bank (click on 'How to use the HSC Resource

Bank'). As you may have noticed, the resource bank provides other things besides information. For example, it includes exercises to help you develop skills of various kinds. When you have a moment to spare, it is worth browsing around the resource bank to see what else might be useful to you.

3.2 Looking back – looking forward

Now that you are more or less halfway through K101, this is a good time to look back and think about how things have gone for you, and also to look ahead to what you want to achieve in the rest of the course, and beyond.

How have you progressed with your learning skills?

In three months of studying, you must have learned a lot, not just about health and social care, but about how to manage the learning process. Being an independent adult student is a big challenge, especially if you haven't studied for a while – and of course, it is vital that you don't waste your precious time studying in ineffective ways. That is why developing your learning skills is given such prominence in K101.

DVD

Activity 4   Reviewing your learning skills

Allow about 30 minutes

So, how much progress have you made with your learning skills since the start of the course? And how can you get the most from the remainder of K101? This activity will help you to review your progress and rethink your strategies.

Find Block 3, Unit 12, Activity 4 on the DVD.

Comment

An activity like this relies on your own assessment of your skills and your progress, so it doesn't tell you how you compare with other students. (That is something you could explore in the online forums.) But actually, it is your own judgement of your learning skills which is most important, since you are the person in charge of your studies. This activity links to a similar activity in the final unit of K101, so that you will be able to see how your perceptions of your strengths and weaknesses as a student change over the second half of the course.

Learning skills: Being an insightful self-manager of your studies

As an independent student, you have to be 'manager' of your studies and of yourself (see Chapter 2 of *The Good Study Guide*). The learning skills strand of K101 stresses the importance of reflecting on your ways of working, so that you can think strategically about how you learn and how best to plan your studies. Rather than just ploughing ahead and hoping for the best, you need to take account of your personal abilities, interests and long-term goals. An exercise like the self-rating profile is a way of sneaking up on yourself to catch a glimpse behind your usual assumptions about yourself. The idea is to stimulate habits of self-reflection and self-analysis, which will enable you to be a flexible and effective self-manager of your studies.

What might you study next year?

Although you are just halfway through the course, this is a good time to start thinking about what you might study *after* K101. Starting now will give you time to explore the options, seek advice, mull things over and still be able to register in good time. Also, registering for your next course fairly soon will help to give focus and a sense of direction to the rest of your K101 studies. You can always change your mind later if your circumstances alter.

Whether or not you feel ready to choose your next course, it is worth finding out a little about how to do it, and the advice that is available to you. Activity 5 takes you on a quick tour.

DVD

Activity 5   Choosing a course

Allow about 30 minutes

There is plenty to think about when choosing a future course, and lots of advice available. To find out more, go to Block 3, Unit 12, Activity 5 on the DVD.

Comment

You should now be clearer about what courses and qualifications are most likely to be of interest to you for next year or subsequent years.

A first look at the exam

There is still plenty of time before it's worth focusing a lot of attention on the exam. However, it is useful to take a quick look, so that you don't get too anxious about it. Between now and the exam we will occasionally take a break to explore aspects of preparing for an exam and developing a strategy, starting now by looking at what kind of an exam it is.

The nature of the exam

The first thing to say about the exam is that *it is designed to help you to do well*. The K101 team does not believe in 'trick questions'. We want you to have every opportunity to use the knowledge and the writing skills you are developing as you work through the course. Our ideal is that your exam result should be very similar to your assignment marks. If you are doing a reasonable proportion of the course reading and sending in your assignments, then you are already preparing yourself well for the exam.

On the other hand, it is important not to be taken by surprise, so you begin by looking at what the exam actually asks you to do.

Activity 6   The guidance in the Assessment Guide

Allow about 20 minutes

Find your Assessment Guide and look for the exam in the contents list.

Read the section on the exam, noting how many questions you need to answer, and how the paper is structured.

Comment

The exam is designed to allow you some choice in preparing for it. You are asked to answer one question on the first two blocks of K101, one question on Blocks 3 to 5, and one question on Block 6. It will be very obvious which questions go with which blocks, as they will have the same numbers. That means you cannot be taken by surprise. You may want to give yourself a bit of room for choice between questions, but you do not have to revise the whole course (unless, of course, you want to).

Another significant point is that you can take a specially prepared sheet of notes into the exam. Indeed, you are encouraged to do this and you will be given plenty of guidance on how to prepare it. So you don't need to worry about your mind going blank in the exam. You will have with you a handy reminder of key items.

You will be sent Specimen Exam Papers, to show you what to expect. This is a key guide in working out how to revise, so read it carefully. You will be coming to all these things in good time, but for now the main message is that the exam is not something to worry about. If you approach it calmly and realistically, and take notice of the advice in the course material and from your tutor, you have every reason to expect to do well.

Special circumstances

If you have a particular reason for anticipating difficulty with the exam, whether because of disability or not being able to attend an exam centre, special arrangements can be made. You can find out more by going to StudentHome: click on the 'Study Support' tab, then on 'Skills for OU study', then on 'Revising, exams and assessment', and you will see a section on 'Alternative arrangements for your exam'. Special arrangements can usually be made where circumstances require, but they need to be set up in advance, so enquire in good time.

3.3 Developing your writing skills

Finally, you return again to the theme of writing skills. At the end of Block 2, you looked at the process of writing and how it can be broken down into stages. Now you go back to the matter of working out what is expected in an essay. At the end of Block 1, you read the first three sections of Chapter 10 of *The Good Study Guide*, focusing on the importance of argument and structure. Now you read the next three sections, which focus on the importance of using your own words but writing clearly and directly.

IVR   Reader

Activity 7   Writing clearly and directly in your own words

Allow about an hour and 20 minutes

Read Sections 10.4 to 10.6 of *The Good Study Guide* **(pages 262–82).**

Comment

Finding your own 'writing voice' is one of the core challenges of studying at degree level. Knowledge is not really useful to you until you can put it into words – your *own* words. But you also need to develop skill in saying things 'the right way', so that they are properly understood. Surprisingly perhaps, this involves trying to say things simply and directly – not 'dressing them up' in elaborate language. All this takes time. Even as you get to higher levels of study, you will still be developing your writing voice. The important thing is to know what you are trying to achieve. The reading and activities you have just done have given you some important pointers. Now you can try following them as you write your next assignment.

End-of-block assignment

You have finished your reading for Block 3, and it is time to write your assignment, TMA 04. Details of TMA 04 can be found in the Assessment Guide.

References

Brain Injury Rehabilitation Trust (undated) *Community Services* [online], www.birt. co.uk/index.asp (Accessed 17 March 2008).

Palmer, G., MacInnes, T. and Kenway, P. (2007) *Monitoring Poverty and Social Exclusion*, York, Joseph Rowntree Foundation [online], www.jrf.org.uk/knowledge/ findings/socialpolicy/2164.asp (Accessed 21 February 2008).

Together (2008) *What is a Community Support Service?* [online], www.together-uk.org/ index.asp?id=141&cachefixer=cf165343884243583#section2 (Accessed 17 March 2008).

Course team

Production team

Andrew Northedge (Chair)

Joanna Bornat (Deputy Chair)

Corinne De Souza (Course Manager)

Maureen Richards (Course Manager)

Sarah Shelley (Course Team Assistant)

Dorothy Atkinson

Fiona Barnes

Ken Blakemore

Hilary Brown

Joyce Cavaye

Anne Fletcher

Marion Hall

Julia Johnson

Rebecca Jones

Ann Martin

Mo McPhail

Ingrid Nix

Sheila Peace

Mary Twomey

Jan Walmsley

Naomi Watson

Fran Wiles

Media production team

Phil Greaney, Fiona Harris, Matthew Moran, Jenny Nockles (Editorial Media Developers); Paul Bishop, Ray Guo (Interactive Media Developers); Vicky Eves (Graphic Artist); Debbie Crouch (Designer); Judy Thomas (Librarian); Adrian Bickers, Michelle Woolley (Media Project Managers); Philippa Broadbent, Ann Carter, Kim Dulson, Siggy Martin (Print Buyers); Sas Amoah, Bisiola Arogundade (Media Assistants); Martin Chiverton (Executive Sound and Vision Producer); Carole Brown (Sound and Vision Assistant); Gail Block, Melisa Ekdoghan, Phil Gauron, Annie Morgan (Clear Focus Productions); Lindsay Brigham, Phil Coleman (Integrated Vocational Route); Richard Norris, Harry Venning (Cartoonists).